Testing
to Verify Design
and Manufacturing
Readiness

Practical Engineering Guides for Managing Risk

by AT&T and the Department of the Navy

Design to Reduce Technical Risk
Design's Impact on Logistics
Moving a Design into Production

Testing
to Verify Design
and Manufacturing
Readiness

AT&T

McGraw-Hill, Inc.

New York   San Francisco   Washington, D.C.   Auckland   Bogotá
Caracas   Lisbon   London   Madrid   Mexico City   Milan
Montreal   New Delhi   San Juan   Singapore
Sydney   Tokyo   Toronto

Library of Congress Cataloging-in-Publication Data

Testing to verify design and manufacturing readiness / AT&T.
    p.   cm. — (Practical engineering guides for managing risks)
    ISBN 0-07-002566-5
    1. Testing. 2. Computer software—Testing. 3. Design,
Industrial—Testing. I. American Telephone and Telegraph Company.
II. Series.
TA410.T43 1993
658.5—dc20   92-41811
                                                CIP

1 2 3 4 5 6 7 8 9 0 DOC/DOC 9 9 8 7 6 5 4 3

ISBN 0-07-002566-5

The sponsoring editor for this book was Robert W. Hauserman, the editing supervisor was Jim Halston, and the production supervisor was Donald F. Schmidt. This book was set in Century Schoolbook. It was composed by McGraw-Hill's Professional Book Group composition unit.

Printed and bound by R. R. Donnelley & Sons Company.

Contents

How This Book Is Organized

This book has five major sections:

Introduction: Contains template definitions, explains which templates are covered, gives risks for each template, and states briefly how to reduce the risks.

Procedures: Presents the steps for reducing the risks for each template covered in this book.

Application: Gives examples for the principles and procedures discussed in the Procedures chapter.

Summary: Outlines information from earlier chapters.

References: Gives an annotated bibliography of sources for more information.

Acknowledgments

The following individuals and their respective organizations are hereby recognized for their contributions to the development of the texts on Practical Engineering Guides for Managing Risk.

Bell Labs, Holmdel, New Jersey

Dr. Robert D. Lake

Dr. Margaret Judith Doran

George J. Hudak

David A. Britman

Ann D. Wright

Gus de los Reyes

Upendra Chivukula

Dr. Blake Patterson

Dr. Howard H. Helms

Dr. Behrooz Khorramian

Julie Strachie

David B. Demyan

Valerie Mehlig

Federal Systems, Greensboro, North Carolina

James H. Everett

Robert S. Doar

David L. Hall

Teresa B. Tucker

Clydy D. Gann

Doug H. Weeks

Russell M. Pennington

J. Gil Jasso

Albert T. Mankowski

**Office of Assistant Secretary of the Navy
(Research, Development & Acquisition)
Product Integrity Directorate, Washington,
D.C.**

Willis J. Willoughby, Jr.

Douglas O. Patterson

Edward L. Smith, Jr.

George E. Maccubbin

Louis C. Gills

Joseph G. Cady

General Electric, Arlington, Virginia

William A. Finn

Elwood P. Padgett, Jr.

Test

Introduction

To the Reader

Part 1, Test, includes seven templates: Integrated Test; Failure Reporting System; Design Limit; Life; Test, Analyze, and Fix (TAAF); Uniform Test Report; and Field Feedback.

The templates, which reflect engineering fundamentals as well as industry and government experience, were first proposed in the early 1980s by a Defense Science Board task force of industry and government leaders, chaired by Willis J. Willoughby, Jr. The task force sought to improve the effectiveness of the transition from development to production of systems. The task force concluded that most program failures were due to a lack of understanding of the engineering and manufacturing disciplines used in the acquisition process. The task force then focused on identifying engineering processes and control methods that minimize technical risks in both government and industry. It defined these critical events in design, test, and production in terms of templates.

The Template Methodology and Documents

A template specifies:

- areas of technical risk
- fundamental engineering principles and proven procedures to reduce the technical risks

Like classical mechanical templates, these templates identify critical measures and standards. By using the templates, developers are more likely to follow engineering disciplines.

In 1985, the task force published 47 templates in the DoD *Transition from Development to Production* (DoD 4245.7-M) manual.[1] The templates cover design, test, production, management, facilities, and logistics.

In 1986, the Department of the Navy issued the *Best Practices* (NAVSO P-6071) manual,[2] which illuminates DoD practices that increase risks. For each template, the *Best Practices* manual describes:

- potential traps and practices that increase the technical risks
- consequences of failing to reduce the technical risks
- an overview of best practices to reduce the technical risks

The *Best Practices* manual seeks to make practitioners more aware of traps and pitfalls so they can avoid repeating mistakes.

In September 1987, the Army Materiel Command made the templates the foundation for their risk reduction roadmaps for program managers.[3] In February 1991, the templates were incorporated into the DoD 5000.2 document as part of a core of fundamental policies and procedures for acquisition programs.[4]

The Templates Are the Foundation for Current Educational Efforts

In 1988, the government initiated an educational program, "Templates: Professionalizing the Acquisition Work Force." This program includes courses and books, such as this one, that increase awareness and promote the use of good engineering practices.

The key to improving the DoD's acquisition process is recognizing that the process is an industrial process, not an administrative process. This is a change in perspective that implies a change in the skills and technical knowledge of the acquisition work force in government and industry. Many in this work force do not have engineering backgrounds. Those with engineering backgrounds often do not have broad experience in design, test, or production. The work force must under-

---

[1]Department of Defense. *Transition from Development to Production*. DoD 4245.7-M, September 1985.

[2]Department of the Navy. *Best Practices: How to Avoid Surprises in the World's Most Complicated Technical Process*. NAVSO P-6071, March 1986.

[3]U.S. Army Materiel Command. *Program Management Risk Reduction Roadmaps*. Alexandria, VA: U.S. Army Materiel Command, September 1987.

[4]Department of Defense. *DoD Instruction 5000.2. Defense Acquisition Management Policies and Procedures*. Washington, DC: Department of Defense, February 23, 1991.

stand basic design, test, and production processes and associated technical risks. The basis for this understanding should be the templates which highlight the critical areas of technical risk.

The template educational program meets the needs of the acquisition work force. The program consists of a series of courses and technical books. The books provide background information for the templates. Each part within the books covers one or more closely related templates.

How the Parts Relate to the Templates

The parts describe:

- the templates, within the context of the overall acquisition process
- risks for each included template
- best commercial practices currently used to reduce the risks
- examples of how these best practices are applied

The parts do not discuss government regulations, standards, and specifications, because these topics are well-covered in other documents and courses. Instead, the parts stress the technical disciplines and processes required for success.

Clustering several templates in one part makes sense when their best practices are closely related. For example, the best practices for the templates in the Parts Selection and Defect Control of *Design to Reduce Technical Risk* interrelate and occur iteratively within design and manufacturing. Designers, suppliers, and manufacturers all have important roles. Other templates, such as Design Reviews, relate to many other templates and thus are best dealt with individually in other books.

Courses on the templates

This book is part of a series that have been designed to be used either in courses or as stand-alone documents. An introductory course on the templates and several technical courses will be available soon.

The courses will help government and industry program managers understand the templates and their underlying engineering disciplines. The managers should recognize that adherence to engineering discipline is more critical to reducing technical risk than strict adherence to government military standards. They should especially recognize when their actions (or inactions) increase technical risks as well as when their actions reduce technical risks.

The Templates Are Models

The templates defined in DoD 4245.7-M are not the final word on disciplined engineering practices or reducing technical risks. Instead, the templates are references and models that engineers and managers can apply to their industrial processes. Companies should look for high-risk technical areas by examining their past projects, by consulting their experienced engineers, and by considering industry-wide issues. The result of these efforts should be a list of areas of technical risk and best practices which becomes the company's own version of the DoD 4245.7-M and NAVSO P-6071 documents. Companies should tailor the best practices and engineering principles described in this book to suit their particular needs. Several military suppliers have already produced manuals tailored to their processes.

Figure 1 shows where to find more and more details about risks, best practices, and engineering principles. Participants in the acquisition process should refer to these resources.

This part covers testing in system development and production. It also urges timely feedback of field experience to improve the system. Its purpose is to make testing timely, efficient, and thorough and to ensure conversion of test results into system improvements.

Testing occurs throughout the development and production of a complex system. Tests evaluate design alternatives. Tests of a prototype or model system verify that the design will work. Tests during develop-

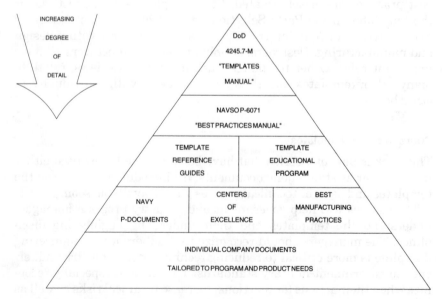

Figure 1 Information about acquisition-process.

ment help refine the design and verify that the subsystems and system work in typical and worst-case mission environments for the life of the system. Acceptance tests by the customer confirm that the system operates well enough to fulfill its mission. Test results and failure experiences from the field help improve the design and performance.

A critical issue with any system is how well it survives after it leaves the factory. All systems face a variety of mission environments, and all systems age. Because some system problems first surface in the field, feedback from the field must occur to guide system improvements.

Before each development test, someone plans the test by choosing who, when, what, and how from lists suggested by Figure 2.

This part discusses DoD 4245.7-M templates:

- Integrated Test
- Failure Reporting System
- Uniform Test Report
- Test, Analyze, and Fix (TAAF)
- Design Limit
- Life
- Field Feedback

Part 2 covers Software Test.

Other books in this series contain additional information on the topics of Figure 2:

- *Design for Testing* covers Design for Testing and Built-In Test
- *Parts Selection and Defect Control* discusses environmental-stress screening and failure-mode analysis for subsystems and piece parts
- *Strategic Manufacturing Planning* covers Manufacturing Plan and Special Test Equipment (STE)

A separate chapter covers each of the seven templates of this part. Each template chapter introduces the template, lists risks avoided by the template, discusses those risks, and explains the template procedures that avoid risk.

Indicators of Success in a Testing Program

Some indicators of success in managing a testing program are:

- Test objectives, test methods, and resource needs are clear and well documented

What

Functional test
Performance test
Environmental-stress screening
Design Limit test*
Life test*
Software test**
Diagnostic test
Maintainability demonstration
Reliability-qualification test
Reliability-development test
EMI test
Documentation-useability test
Etc.

* =Template in this part

** =Template in another book
in this series

How

Design for Testing**
Built-In Test**
Failure Reporting System*
Uniform Test Report*
Test, Analyze, and Fix*
Special Test Equipment (STE)**
People to run tests & analyze results
Special environments & locations
Items submitted for testing
Documentation
Funding
Etc.

Who

Customer
 - Procuring organization
 - Independent organization
 - Users
Project management
Prime contractor
Subcontractor

When

Concept exploration
Demonstration/Validation
Development
Qualification
Operational (system) testing
Production acceptance
Production

Figure 2 Domain of test management.

- The test effort and its schedules have high priority in system development

- The data collected during testing meets everyone's needs and appears in a standard format

- The test plan emphasizes reliability growth

- The test effort involves the systematic collection, analysis, and review of all test results and failures

- Appropriate tools and methods for analyzing and preventing failures are available

- After identifying the root causes of failures, designers change the system to prevent their recurrence

2

Integrated Test

This part focuses on the management of testing in system development and production. Its purpose is to make testing timely, efficient, and thorough and to ensure conversion of test results into system improvements.

Adequate testing is essential from the development phase of a contract through initial production to ensure that the product meets its requirements. History shows that poor test planning in the early phases of program development results in problems in service.

Introduction

Today's contracts typically call for performing a series of tests as part of the development process. These tests often have not been coordinated with each other and may not be sufficient. Conversely, subsystem testing often far exceeds common sense.

Many test scenarios are developed by prime contractors and subcontractors independently of specific contract requirements. This is particularly true at the subsystem level, where the contractor decides which tests are necessary. Many of the tests also are planned by different design groups in the contractor's facility and are not necessarily coordinated at the program level. This causes redundant testing and degrades the efficiency of the test process.

Although most programs have a defined test plan, this plan is usually a top-level set of test requirements that are not properly integrated with each other. Because of this, redundant testing occurs in certain instances, too-stringent testing in some instances, and lack of adequate testing in other instances.

Risks Avoided by Integrated Test

This template describes *integrated* planning and coordination of testing among the system team—the prime contractor, subcontractors, and the customer (e.g., the government). Integration includes the careful accounting of objectives, environments, test-article configurations, data requirements, and schedules. Recognizing that test and evaluation are major cost drivers, the objectives of test integration are to minimize overlaps and gaps, to collect maximum intelligence from every test, and to ensure a smooth and effective test program at minimum cost. The absence of a carefully integrated test plan is a certain indicator of a high-risk program (see Table 1).

Risk: Critical tests are omitted

Pressed by costs and schedules, contractors or the government may omit key tests by oversight, by failing to consult technical experts, or because those tests seem unimportant. Omission of key tests can lead to unpleasant surprises later.

Sometimes designers test what they designed rather than what the customer specified in requirements. In other words, designers become so immersed in the system that they advocate tests that show off its capabilities. If creativity causes them to lose sight of the customer's needs, they and test planners may omit tests that could reveal mission-compromising flaws.

Test planners sometimes omit subsystem tests because they believe the subsystem is "qualified by similarity," i.e., an identical or similar

TABLE 1   Risks and Consequences of Not Taking an Integrated Approach to Testing

Risks	Consequences
Critical tests are omitted	Design shortcomings may appear after the system has been deployed
Tests are duplicated	Development costs are too high, and schedules are affected
Test resources are inadequate	Tests are delayed, results are incomplete, results are inaccurate, system faults are missed, and system performance suffers
Test schedules are uncoordinated	There is inadequate time for testing, tests occur in the wrong sequence, tests compete for critical test equipment, test requirements aren't met, etc.
Schedules are milestone-oriented	Test results seem to confirm progress, but they do not cause needed system improvement

subsystem proved adequate in a similar system, and test planners assume that this ensures the subsystem will satisfy the needs of the current system *without testing*. Real differences between the similar system and the current system may contradict this assumption. The result of omitting tests may be a nonworking, unreliable, or unsafe system.

Test planners sometimes omit certain subsystem tests because the people who are aware of the need for these tests are not members of the test-planning team. The resulting holes in the test plan can jeopardize the system and its mission.

Risk: Tests are duplicated

Unnecessary costs result if contractors, subcontractors, or the customer duplicate the same test. Because testing resources are limited, duplicate testing can also delay system availability.

For example, during Development Test and Evaluation (DT&E), which is performed to verify attainment of technical performance specifications, the contractor and the government normally conduct separate, dedicated tests.[5] In many instances these separate tests result in redundant testing, testing that is not user-oriented, lack of continuity in the contractor's development program, and a lack of cooperation between contractor and government personnel.

Contractors and the government may waste time trying to reconcile slightly different results from nearly identical tests. This is a hidden or secondary cost of duplicate testing.

Risk: Test resources are inadequate

A lack of resources can jeopardize the testing schedule and, consequently, the whole project. Needed resources include the system being tested, the equipment that does the testing, and people who run the test.

Equipment that is available but unusable because of disrepair, old age, or other defect, may mislead planners into believing that resources are adequate.

An example of inadequate test equipment occurred in the Hardened Intersite Cable System.[6] Specifically, the equipment that located faults in the wire pairs detected only short circuits, but not open circuits. When electrical failures caused testers to check the wiring, the fault-finding equipment showed that there were no short circuits in the wiring. Actually, one or more open-circuit wires caused the failure, but

---

[5]DoD 5000.2, p. 8-2.

[6]Aeronautic Division of Wright-Patterson AFB. *Generic Integrated Maintenance Diagnostics (GIMADS) Task 12*. Draft of February 19, 1990, p. D-190.

testers wasted time tracing other possible causes because the wiring tester implied perfect wiring.

Risk: Test schedules are uncoordinated

Often planners establish test schedules with little consideration of the purpose of each test or the interrelation of various tests with each other. Test schedules may slip because testers do not perform critical tests in the proper sequence, or planners do not allow time for redesign and retest. Additionally, if planners fail to consider test phasing, they may schedule a multitude of tests at the same time, and testers may lack critical test equipment.

Risk: Schedules are milestone-oriented

Most test schedules support the major milestone reviews that occur during the development of a system. The tests provide positive (successful) test results for presentation at these milestone reviews to obtain approval for the project to proceed to the next milestone. This leads to a test philosophy in which passing tests is the main objective of the test program, rather than considering the engineering need for the test or the technical information provided by the test results. As a result, test schedules tend to be success-oriented, many times resulting in schedule slippage because of the need for retest or a lack of test assets.

Procedures

Integrated:...Composed of separate parts united together to form a...complete, harmonious, or coordinated entity...Characterized by close cooperation or partial unity of constituent units...[7]

The Integrated Test template requires coordinated planning to ensure proper time-phasing of all development tests, availability of adequate resources (e.g., test articles, test facilities, funding, and people), and elimination of duplicate or redundant testing.

Because testing strongly drives cost and schedule, adequate planning is essential long before the start of any testing. A successful Integrated Test program requires coordination between the government, the prime contractor, and all subcontractors. Test planning should start with program initiation.

---

[7]*Webster's Third New International Dictionary, Unabridged.* Springfield, MA: G. C. Merriam, 1968, p. 628.

In integrated testing the government, its prime contractor, and its subcontractors must cooperate as a team, mutually supporting each other and striving to achieve a successful test program. They must recognize the importance of testing to verify that each component, subsystem, and ultimately the entire system meets the users' needs.

Test enough but only enough

The object of cooperative testing is testing that is thorough enough to ensure success but avoids duplication of testing and test resources. For example, the contractor responsible for an airplane's landing gear may not own a wind tunnel. That contractor could pay for a new test facility or, alternatively, could conserve resources by using the air-frame contractor's wind tunnel. Although the second option requires that contractors share the test facility, this cooperation can save money and perhaps also enable the project to move ahead faster. Many times, cooperation is a "win-win" situation in which everyone gains something.

Achieving a balance between too little and too much testing is not easy:

- Not doing a *key* test can cause mission failure.

- On the other hand, the value of testing a non-essential component, like an ash tray or cigarette lighter, may never justify the cost of testing.

- Test planners should avoid duplicate tests, since these result in the government "paying double." Nevertheless, sometimes it is necessary to re-check mission-critical or safety-related capabilities. For example, repeated tests of a pilot ejection mechanism, which is expensive and time-consuming, may prevent a fatality.

Sometimes developers avoid testing and its cost by putting in the new system a subsystem that proved itself reliable in a similar system. Such subsystems are "Non-Development Items" and may be "qualified by similarity."

Is it necessary to retest a "qualified by similarity" subsystem? Answering this question requires comparing the original and new environments carefully. For example, the EA-6B Prowler aircraft's incoming-missile warning system had been "qualified by similarity," but failed in the new system. Changes to the aircraft's engine focused acoustic waves on the warning system and caused destructive vibration.

Limits to cooperation

There are limits to government-contractor cooperation, of course, because the government must ensure that the system meets end-user needs, while contractors need only satisfy the contract. The government ensures satisfied end-users through tests of its own, or it can witness tests run by contractors.

Another limit to cooperation is the contractors' need for profit—they may go out of business without it—which discourages them from running unfunded tests. Contractors may not schedule a test if the need to do it arises after signing contracts, unless the government provides additional funds. The contractor may agree that the test is important and may want to do it, but contractor survival may dictate the need for extra payment for extra testing.

Management of integrated test

The tests required to develop, produce, and maintain modern weapon systems are complex, extensive, and expensive. Proven test-management concepts developed and demonstrated during prior programs must be used during development and production.

Program office.   The program office is responsible for the overall management of the test program. Test-program direction, test-program changes, test policy, and budget authorization are established through the program office.

Test Planning Team (TPT).   In this ideal model, project management sets up a Test-Planning Team (TPT) that includes technically competent people who represent the government, each contractor, and the eventual users of the system. The TPT is responsible for test planning and coordination that best meets the needs of the project. The TPT commits to holding periodic (e.g., weekly) meetings (e.g., by teleconferencing) until testers finish testing, data analysts sift test results, root-cause analysts study failure modes, and designers improve the system. A small project may not need a TPT, but someone in project management will have to fulfill this function.

The TPT provides a central test planning-and-integrating function to ensure proper support to the program and optimum use of all test resources. It provides a forum for assembling and evaluating test program objectives, plans, and programs, for resolving conflicts and inconsistencies in schedules and priorities, for evaluating and reporting progress, and for realigning the tests as program changes occur.

Early in the program the TPT develops test guidelines and instructions by coordinating and reviewing documents that define test programs, requirements, schedules, and scope. The TPT then assures integration of the total test program.

The TPT is composed of representatives from each major government, contractor, and subcontractor organization. It functions as an arm of the program office.

Test integration

Integrated Test planning has two fundamental tasks. The first is to select the right tests: those for which the need is greatest. The second is to ensure that these selected tests are done in a way that maximizes the payoff from the resource invested. Together, these two produce the greatest increase in confidence achievable with the available resource. In practice, neither of these is a one-time job. Test selection and design may require refining even after final plans are set in motion to accommodate last-minute changes made necessary by mission-profile or operational data that are more up-to-date, or by the results of other tests.

The Integrated Test planning flow, summarized in Figure 3, includes both tasks. It is built around a test planning form that serves as a checklist to remind the test planner of issues that need decisions.

The overall flow aids the test planner in several ways:

- Test policies and ground rules establish fundamentals that the test must comply with.
- The test planning forms summarize test objectives, test hardware, support equipment, and facility requirements.
- The condensed description of each test on the planning forms simplifies communication and integration with interfacing organizations.

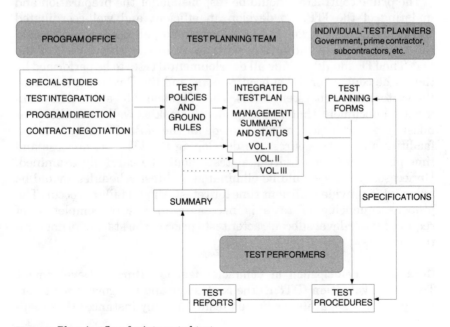

Figure 3 Planning flow for integrated test.

This flow of documentation also aids program management:

- The planning forms provide a visible bridge from program objectives to the tests that implement them.
- Form entries make the cost-versus-risk trade-off more objective. (Costs may be estimated from the test definition, and areas of insufficient testing are exposed by matrices showing the number of test articles dedicated to the various tests.)
- Test planning assessment from a total program perspective by the TPT ensures that program constraints and milestones are satisfied.

Integrated test plan

The Integrated Test Plan (ITP), which is sometimes called the Test-and-Evaluation Master Plan (TEMP) or Test-and-Evaluation Program Plan (TEPP), has three purposes. First, it integrates the various test programs to obtain maximum amounts of data at the required time with a minimum cost in program resources. Second, it describes all test-program activity so that the contractor and the government have the necessary information to manage test integration. Third, it relates test requirements to critical program milestones, defining test-data usage and test completion requirements so that test data are available to support milestone decisions.

The prime contractor should be responsible for the preparation and updating of the ITP. To develop an efficient and well-coordinated Integrated Test program, the prime contractor, all subcontractors, and the government should jointly participate in the preparation of the ITP. The ITP should include all developmental tests to be performed by the prime contractor, all subcontractors, and the Government at both the system and subsystem levels. The ITP should be a detailed working-level document that will help identify risk as well as duplicate or missing test activities and will provide for the most efficient use of test facilities and test resources. In developing the ITP, the purpose and time-phasing of each individual test should be carefully examined. Unnecessary tests should be eliminated and test schedules should be adjusted to provide sufficient time for retest, should failures occur. The proper sequencing of tests is necessary to ensure completion of required lower-level subcontractor tests prior to the start of prime-contractor tests.

Government participation in contractor testing. During Development Test and Evaluation (DT&E) the contractor and the government normally conduct separate, dedicated tests. In many instances these separate test periods result in redundant testing, testing that is not user-oriented, lack of continuity in the contractor's development program, and a lack of cooperation between contractor and government personnel. In order to increase the efficiency of DT&E, the government should participate in some of the contractor's testing. This will help eliminate redundant testing, reduce the length of DT&E phases, provide test results that are more user-oriented, and result in a more mature system for Operational Test and Evaluation (OT&E).

Development Test and Evaluation (DT&E)

- identifies potential operational and technological limitations of the alternative concepts and design options being pursued
- supports the identification of cost-performance trade-offs
- supports the identification and description of design risks
- substantiates that contract technical performance and manufacturing process requirements have been achieved
- supports the decision to certify the system ready for operational test and evaluation

Operational Test and Evaluation (OT&E) programs determine the operational effectiveness and suitability of a system under realistic mission conditions and determine whether the system satisfies the minimum acceptable operational performance requirements as specified in the Test-and-Evaluation Master Plan (TEMP).

Operational Test and Evaluation

- uses threat-representative forces whenever possible
- employs typical users to operate and maintain the system or item, under conditions simulating combat stress and peacetime conditions
- uses production or production-representative articles for the dedicated phase of OT&E that supports the decision on full-rate production

Figure 4 shows the DT&E that occurs during system development.[8] It contains more detail than this overview will discuss, but it shows that DT&E starts early in development. DT&E assesses the feasibility of design alternatives and continues through early operation of the system in the field when it helps find problems that may degrade performance and increase production risk.

---

[8]Defense Systems Management College. *Test and Evaluation Management Guide.* Fort Belvoir, VA: DSMC, March 1988, p. 8-2.

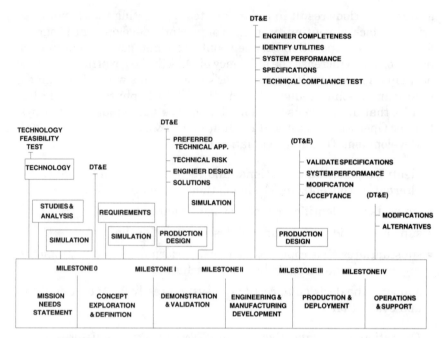

Figure 4 DT&E during system acquisition.

Figure 5 shows the OT&E that occurs during system development, also in more detail than this book will discuss.[9]

OT&E begins early in development and continues through early operations. OT&E acts as a sanity check. For example, OT&E during the Concept Exploration and Definition phase assesses:

- the physical basis for the new system
- the concept's ability to satisfy the military need
- the system's affordability and life-cycle cost
- the existing system's ability to fill the same need
- the system's operational prospects

Although DT&E and OT&E nominally have different sponsors and employ different testers and analysts, they often call for the same or

---

[9]Defense Systems Management College. *Test and Evaluation Management Guide.* Fort Belvoir, VA: DSMC, March 1988, p. 10-2.

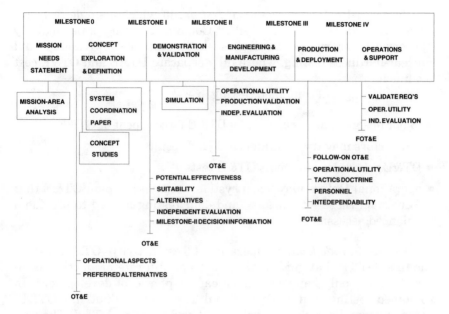

Figure 5 OT&E during system acquisition.

similar tests, and this similarity provides the opportunity for integrating efforts of the contractors and the government.

One option is *concurrent testing,* in which development testing and operational testing occur at the same time but are done on different equipment at different test sites.[10] This limited test integration shortens the testing time and the acquisition cycle. Concurrent testing brings operational testers and developers together (e.g., as they plan the sharing of scarce system prototypes), and that proximity caused by concurrent testing may get operational concerns to developers quickly and speed design changes.

Disadvantages of concurrent testing are:

- DT&E may cause major design changes that force operational testers to repeat OT&E for the revamped system
- DT&E schedules may limit OT&E tests

Despite these disadvantages, contractors and the government like concurrent, cooperative testing.

---

[10]Defense Systems Management College. *Test and Evaluation Management Guide.* Fort Belvoir, VA: DSMC, March 1988, p. 17-1.

A lower-cost option is *combined testing,* in which a single test program supports DT&E and OT&E.[11] Combined testing is particularly appropriate for special testing, such as nuclear-survivability and nuclear-hardness testing, where fully separate DT&E and OT&E cost too much.

Disadvantages of combined testing are:

- major design changes caused by DT&E force repeat of OT&E
- contractors may try to influence OT&E results
- DT&E schedules may limit OT&E tests
- operational testers may learn system weaknesses, plan OT&E that focuses on those weaknesses, and omit testing needed to provide a balanced assessment

Because an *independent* Operational Test Activity (OTA) must do the final OT&E that guides the decision on full-rate production, combined testing only happens during earlier phases of development. In combined testing, Initial Operational Test and Evaluation (IOT&E) begins informally early in development and parallels DT&E. The government's IOT&E group and the contractors' DT&E groups share data for mutual benefit. They arrange tests that satisfy the needs of developers and operational evaluators. Combined testing offers more opportunities for efficient test integration than concurrent testing.

Combined testing helped the F-14 Tomcat fighter aircraft succeed.[12] A key was selection of a test-and-evaluation coordinator who supervised test planning that integrated the technical needs of developers with the operational needs of users. That coordinator also allocated test resources and managed tests. Most development tests and operational tests took place during the same period and even on the same flights. Navy testers *witnessed,* i.e., observed and accepted, contractor demonstrations to avoid duplicate testing.

Design the tests. The Test Planning Team (TPT) assigns responsibility for designing key tests. Test designers are typically contractors' employees, but the government's experts design operational tests. The design effort ranges from high-level planning to the detailed design and creation of hardware and software used in testing.

---

[11]Defense Systems Management College. *Test and Evaluation Management Guide.* Fort Belvoir, VA: DSMC, March 1988, p. 17-1.

[12]Hoivik, Thomas H. "The Navy Test and Evaluation Process in Major Systems Acquisition." DTIC Accession Number AD A035935, November, 1976.

Should test planners choose state-of-the-art, up-to-date testing methods whenever possible? The benefits are:

- fewer hours of testing
- fewer human errors as automation replaces manual actions
- the possible reuse of test equipment by later projects

Planners must weigh these advantages against the acquisition costs of the latest methods (design, development, or purchase) and the cost of scrapping existing test equipment or supporting still-needed but older equipment.

When testers must develop software to do testing, how can they get a good understanding of the intended function of the system? A clearly written Integrated Test Plan can help, of course, but testers, system designers, and project management need to share information.

Identify who tests and when.   For critical tests, the TPT decides who will do the testing and when. In many cases the TPT assigns a particular contractor. Sometimes several subcontractors combine their efforts, e.g., to test subsystem interactions and interfaces. For example, the subcontractor responsible for tank electrical systems may work with the engine and transmission subcontractors to verify that the tank driver has full control of the mobility subsystem. If the prime contractor is the sole systems integrator, the prime contractor alone may do the systems integration tests that ensure the system meets requirements. Often the government participates in testing. It may provide runways, proving grounds, pilots, or test beds not otherwise available to contractors.

Besides identifying who will design the tests, the TPT estimates the human and test-equipment resources needed for running tests and analyzing and acting on the results of each test. Those estimates will change as test design progresses.

Should the acceptance tests be run entirely by the government? Can some of these tests be *witnessed* by the government or by the government's representative? Who might gain confidence in the system by attending design reviews and Failure Review Board (FRB) meetings? The trend in industry and government is to recognize that acceptance testing is too costly and too time-consuming *not* to be integrated with development and production testing. Hence the combined testing discussed in the previous chapter.

The scheduling of DT&E and OT&E by the TPT relies on estimates of development progress, the need to assess that progress without impairing it, and the need for resources to do the tests. Juggling those often-conflicting needs is a key job of the TPT.

Test planners should phase test schedules primarily on engineering considerations. They should consider the purpose or objective of each test as well as the interrelation of various tests with each other. Because the start of certain tests may depend on the completion of others, test planners should identify critical tests and provide for schedule slippage caused by needed redesign and retest. In certain cases, test planners or testers can do those critical tests early by providing more test articles or additional test facilities. This strategy can significantly reduce the overall development test schedule. Program managers can then plan milestone reviews on the basis of realistic test schedules. Test results that are more engineering-oriented and show design strengths and weaknesses should be presented at design reviews. The review should discuss design weaknesses and how they have been or will be corrected. The overall success of a carefully integrated test program will result in a minimum of resources applied to testing and the elimination of costly engineering changes or retrofit programs during production.

To document the testing process, the TPT oversees the creation of a hierarchy of planning documents:

- the government's Test-and-Evaluation Master Plan (TEMP), a high-level outline of development (DT&E) tests and operational (OT&E) tests, including a general statement of the objective of each series of tests

- the prime contractor's Integrated Test Plan (ITP), which includes all development and qualification tests (prime contractor, subcontractors, and Government) at the system and subsystem levels

- the contractors' individual test plans, which specify details of each test

Usually the government authors the TEMP, the prime contractor authors the ITP, and the contractors responsible for subsystems write the individual test plans for particular tests of each subsystem.

Test objectives begin with the customer's most critical needs given in the system requirements. Those requirements become high-level test requirements in the TEMP. The high-level test requirements grow more specific in the ITP, which drives the individual test plans that detail each test. Conversely, crucial, design-affecting test results flow up from testers, through analysts, designers, and the FRB to project management. Prime-contractor project management then informs the customer as required by the contract.

The TEMP, ITP, and individual test plans evolve along with the development of the system. Test planning is a dynamic activity, with the results of tests and changes to the system determining the need for new tests and test plans.

A later chapter discusses integrated test documents in more detail.

Run the tests and improve the system. Testers designated in the test-planning documents run the tests. They record the results of the test and forward them to analysts who share their findings with the TPT, the FRB, government project management, and affected contractors. The Failure Reporting System's database accepts test results and makes them available to the development team.

If tests yield expected results and confirm that development is on schedule, testing proceeds.

If tests yield unexpected results or imply a problem with the system design:

- the design team analyzes the test results to uncover the root cause of the test problem.[13]
- the analysis is distributed among designers, suppliers, and other relevant parties and proposals to resolve problems are developed.

Do OT&E. When the contractors and project management believe that the system satisfies all requirements, the system goes to an independent testing agency, such as the government's Operational Test Activity (OTA), for independent operational testing.

With the contractors absent, the OTA tests the fitness of the system. The OTA notes needed improvements and specifies new tactics, support organizations, and personnel. The OTA assesses the system's documentation: training manuals that introduce users to system features, handbooks that help users make the best of system features during missions, and operations plans that show how to provision and maintain the system in the field.

The OTA does testing to determine operational effectiveness and suitability under realistic combat conditions.

Production-acceptance testing. Production-acceptance tests show whether or not items (systems, subsystems, and components) comply with the requirements of the contract. They are done at the completion of the manufacturing operation.[14]

---

[13]*Parts Selection and Defect Control* reference guide. pp. 84–85.

[14]Headquarters Naval Material Command. *Navy Program Manager's Guide.* Washington, DC: Department of the Navy, 1985, p. 4-91.

One type of production-acceptance test, sponsored by the Board of Inspection and Survey (BIS), applies only to ships and aircraft.

Production-acceptance tests for items other than ships and aircraft are government acceptance tests (GATs), which include factory acceptance tests (FATs) performed on each item and production-monitoring tests (PMTs).

People who make integrated test happen

Figure 6 shows the human roles associated with the *Integrated Test* template. Project management oversees the TPT and the DT&E groups. The system designers and system fabricators are independent of the TPT, but they contribute to the DT&E process by improving the system in response to test findings. As the vertical dashed line suggests, the OTA, its test designers, and its testers maintain their independence from project management.

Project management.   The government's program manager chooses the Test-Planning Team (TPT) that plans key project tests.

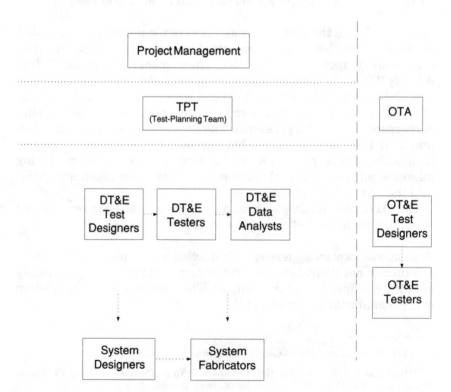

Figure 6 People who support integrated test.

Test-planning team. The TPT outlines test needs based on system requirements and names test designers whose skills match the key tests.

For each test, the TPT chooses a test team that writes the individual test plan, decides what resources are needed, arranges to have those resources ready when and where needed to do the tests, and picks testers who will do the tests and document the results.

The TPT names an analyst or group of analysts for each test. That individual or group will study the test results and report to the program office any recommendations for further action.

The TPT also identifies potential users of test results, such as system designers, production-test-equipment designers, maintenance-test-equipment designers, and project management.

Failure Review Board. A Failure Review Board (FRB) is often established to monitor the performance of certain tests, such as a Reliability-Growth Test, and ensure compliance with contractual requirements.

(The *Failure Reporting System* template, discussed in a later chapter, defines the FRB.)

The FRB will analyze the results of tests and ensure that the system is improved as needed to satisfy mission needs and system requirements.

Operational Test Activity. The OTA is an independent operational test-and-evaluation (OT&E) activity. In the case of the Navy, this activity is the Operational Test-and-Evaluation Force (OPTEVFOR). It is intentionally independent of the procuring agency that oversees system development.

The OTA manages final operational testing, which verifies that the system is ready for users, purchase by the government, and full-scale production by the contractors. The OTA does that final testing in an environment that is as close as possible to mission conditions.

The OTA gives its independent evaluation of the system to the Military Service Chief, Defense Agency Director, or other agency chief.

Authors of test documents. Government experts write the Test-and-Evaluation Master Plan (TEMP), using contractor experts as reviewers, especially for the DT&E section and schedules. Contractor experts write the Integrated Test Plan (ITP) and rely on government experts to check for omission of DT&E tests specified in the TEMP. OTA experts prepare the Operational Test-and-Evaluation Plan and the individual test plans for each final operational test. If the TPT uses combined testing to eliminate the need for duplicate DT&E and OT&E during the initial stages of development, contractor, TPT, and OTA experts may jointly write the individual test plans for IOT&E tests and include these tests in the ITP.

Experts representing the prime contractor and subcontractors write DT&E Individual Test Plans. For example, if a subsystem belongs to a contractor, that contractor's experts write the DT&E individual test plans for that subsystem. If a DT&E test involves several contractors, experts representing each involved contractor may jointly prepare the individual test plan, or the system integrator may prepare it alone.

Test designers. Just as authors of a DT&E individual test plan should represent each contractor involved in the test, the designers of a DT&E test should represent the contractors whose subsystems will be tested. If the TPT uses combined testing, OTA or other contractor-independent experts should ensure that DT&E test designs will provide needed evidence of operability. Test designers from the OTA will generally design the final OT&E to ensure an impartial, operation-oriented, fitness-for-use determination.

Testers. Contractor employees generally conduct DT&E tests, usually witnessed by government representatives. Testers representing the government join with contractors' testers to do DT&E and IOT&E if the TPT specifies combined testing.

Government testers may do DT&E if they have unique capabilities, equipment, or training.

OTA employees do final OT&E tests. They do *all* OT&E if the TPT does not use combined testing.

Test analyzers. Test analyzers representing contractors must find the root causes of undesirable test results and the best ways to eliminate them. They include data specialists who convert raw results into compact pictures of system (or subsystem) performance and failure-mode analysts who find the root causes of unexpected results.

Test analyzers representing the government may use their analyses of test results that are unexpected or undesirable in different ways. For example, if OT&E results are unexpected but surmountable, government analyzers may use them to recommend changes to user training, mission tactics, logistics, or maintenance for the new system. Government analyzers of OT&E tests need the ability to recognize unacceptable results and report them.

Integrated-test documents

The major documents that support *Integrated Test* are the TEMP, the ITP, and individual test plans for development testing and operational testing. These documents support testing aspects of system development and are not key products of that development. The government and contractors should view these documents as aids to integration. The ITP, for example, can reveal duplicate tests and, when compared with system requirements, can show omitted tests. An individual test plan provides test details that confirm whether the actual test fulfills the goal promised in the TEMP or ITP.

Test-and-Evaluation Master Plan.   DoD Instruction 5000.2 requires the preparation of a Test-and-Evaluation Master Plan (TEMP). The TEMP is a broad plan relating test objectives to required system characteristics and critical issues. It is a top-level document used at major-milestone reviews to assess the adequacy of planned test and evaluation. The TEMP normally covers only government-required tests and does not provide enough detail to identify contractor and subcontractor tests. To control the test program at the contractor and subcontractor level, contracts may contain requirements for submitting individual test plans for government approval. If the contractor fails to write the ITP, these individual test plans may not be reviewed for duplicate or missing test activities, resulting in an inefficient and costly test program.

The program manager is responsible for the TEMP. Early on, the program manager or the TPT apportions the writing among the contractors and the government. The operational-testing section is written, for example, by the Operational Test Activity (OTA) that will run the final operational tests.

Though nominally a plan created by the government, the TEMP will drive all other testing and should be a plan that the government creates in cooperation with contractors. Writing the TEMP can begin immediately by listing tests that will have to be done to confirm achievement of system requirements. The TEMP should be complete at the end of the concept-and-evaluation phase of system acquisition, which is early in development. The TEMP is a living document and will change and mature as system design progresses.

Integrated Test Plan.   Contractors prepare the ITP with joint participation by all subcontractors and the government. The ITP integrates all developer test activities, using the DT&E part of the TEMP as an outline. For a large system, the TPT may decide to create several ITPs, one for each major subsystem. The ITP does not cover OT&E unless the project uses combined testing.

The Integrated Test Plan describes tests required when different subsystems are integrated, coordinates the tests among organizations, and states resource needs.

Individual Test Plans. Before a key development test is done, the TPT assigns responsibility for writing an individual test plan, which describes what will be tested, how it will be tested, when it will be tested, and who will test it. The individual test plan specifies development tests in greater detail than the ITP or TEMP. The contractor responsible for the component, subsystem, or system to be tested generally writes the individual test plan and runs or supervises the test. Sometimes several contractors and the government help run a test.

Before the Operational Test Activity (OTA) does the operational tests listed in the OT&E part of the TEMP, the OTA writes detailed test descriptions, much like the individual test plans written for development tests. The OTA should resolve any ambiguities about requirements or mission objectives with the contracting agency if those ambiguities affect operational tests.

Summary of Integrated Test Template

The planning, people, and documents discussed above can achieve the goals of the *Integrated Test* template.

Those goals are cooperative, efficient, effective, and timely testing that ensures success.

This part cannot prescribe what to test, when to test, how to test, and who should test. Sometimes critical subsystems warrant repeated testing; sometimes noncritical subsystems need no formal testing. Sometimes planners can delay tests if, for example, needed resources will be easier to obtain later, key decisions do not depend on the test results, and confidence in achieving successful results is high. Who should test is often a political decision, especially if cooperation between government and contractors is low, contrary to the goal of *Integrated Test*.

Testing decisions are ultimately engineering decisions. The material in this chapter offers a framework for wise engineering decisions.

Failure Reporting System

Failure Reporting System is a process for recording failures, analyzing them, and taking action to prevent their recurrence.[15] Although several military standards require Failure Reporting System, the implementation of these requirements has been managed poorly, defined improperly, and undisciplined. The flow down of requirements from prime contractor to subcontractors has not been uniform, analysis of all failures has not been required, the timely close-out of failure reports has been overlooked, and systems for alerting higher management to problem areas have been missing. Instances of ineffective and inefficient failure reporting have been documented.[16]

Introduction

The *Failure Reporting System* template describes a methodology, including tools, formats, and managerial procedures, to make certain that all failures are tracked, analyzed, and prevented from recurring.

Risks Avoided by Failure Reporting System

The Procedures chapter explains Failure Reporting System. Table 2 summarizes risks that Failure Reporting System can prevent.

---

[15]*Failure Reporting System* includes "Failure-Reporting, Analysis, and Corrective-Action System," or "FRACAS."

[16]Department of the Navy. *Best Practices—How to Avoid Surprises in the World's Most Complicated Technical Process.* Washington DC; NAVSO P-6071, U.S. Government Printing Office, March 1986, pp. 5–7.

TABLE 2   Risks and Consequences Avoided by Failure Reporting System

Risks	Consequences
Failure Reporting System is not used throughout the project	Subcontractors may not correct important failure modes
Corporate management is not informed about problems	Failure Reporting System is poorly managed and undisciplined. Failure causes are not corrected in a timely manner
The organization controlling the Failure Reporting System is ineffective	Developers do not analyze failures and remedy their causes quickly
Only repeat failures are analyzed	Design flaws cause operational problems and jeopardize mission success
Failure reports remain open too long	Delays in corrective actions cause failures to recur, sometimes during missions
Test failure reports are not stored in a database used by all contractors and the government	Communication of test data and the status of failure reports, failure-mode analysis, and corrective actions is slow and poor

Risk: Failure reporting system is not used throughout the project

Failure Reporting System will work only if it applies to all testing, including that performed by subcontractors and by the government. Otherwise, important failure causes may remain uncorrected; this can cause unnecessary and costly repeating of failures.

For example, testing at the subassembly level by the subcontractor may reveal a design defect. If this defect is left uncorrected, it will recur during testing at higher levels of assembly. This will result in increased cost and schedule delays necessitated by repair of the failed subassembly and possible repeat of the entire test.

Risk: Corporate management is not informed about problems

Failure data that is collected in Failure Reporting System is useful only when aggregated for purposeful evaluation. A failure data system should be designed to collect, store, and retrieve failure information and to provide the means for displaying the data in a meaningful form. The outputs of a failure data system should be tailored to provide summaries and special reports for both management and engineering personnel. The failure summary is a useful output of a failure data system and should provide information that automatically alerts management when failure reports are open too long or when corrective actions are ineffective.

Risk: The organization controlling the failure reporting system is ineffective

If the organization controlling the Failure Reporting System lacks knowledgeable members who have the power to make decisions, they cannot require that developers analyze and correct failures quickly and effectively. Another source of ineffectiveness is inactivity. For example, if this organization needs to hold meetings but does not hold them regularly (e.g., by teleconferencing if it is too difficult to convene face-to-face meetings), it cannot ensure that test results quickly turn into system improvements.

Management may miss problems unless a formal scheme like Failure Reporting System brings them to light. For example, NASA's upper management minimized the danger of booster-seal stiffness at near-freezing temperatures, even though engineers understood that danger. An effective Failure Reporting System might have prevented NASA's *Challenger* disaster.

Risk: Only repeat failures are analyzed

If contractors do not analyze one-time failures, they may miss operational, manufacturing, or design defects that could jeopardize missions. Also, waiting until a failure recurs delays actions that could correct the failure and prevent schedule delays and cost overruns.

Many Japanese companies view every failure as a "treasure" of information. After spending large sums on failure-cause analyses to learn the root causes of all test failures, these companies increased their manufacturing yields and product reliability greatly during the past decade.

Risk: Failure reports remain open too long

Often, the failure reports that developers wait to resolve involve failures that are difficult to analyze or time-consuming or expensive to fix. Project managers may not know that some failures remain unresolved. These lingering reports often reveal problems that can seriously compromise the system's ability to perform its mission.

One reason contractors fail to close out failures is that they do not require a time limit on close-out. Without a set time-limit and a process (such as Failure Reporting System) that assigns responsibility for investigating failures and monitors progress, haphazard closing of failure reports is likely.

Risk: Failure reports are not stored in the database used by contractors

For example, in the Air Force's B-1B Bomber's central integrated test system, subcontractors reported data in different formats, which slowed progress.[17] Converting the data to a standard format corrected this problem.

Risk: Single database is not used throughout the whole project

Today's technology makes it easy to set up a single database that all contractors and the government can use for recording test data, including all failures. If this is not done, the communication of test results will be slowed, and project personnel will find it more difficult to learn the status of failure reports, including their failure-mode analysis and corrective actions. A modern database—particularly a "relational" database—is straightforward to set up and easy to interrogate. Such a database also can reduce the need for project management to distribute test results, since project personnel can obtain test results from the database.

Procedures

The MIL-STD definition of Failure Reporting System is "a closed-loop system for initiating reports, analyzing failures, and feeding back corrective actions into the design, manufacturing, and test processes."[18] The primary objective of Failure Reporting System is to document failures, analyze the causes of failures, determine corrective action, and disseminate the data. The timely dissemination of accurate failure information is necessary so that remedial actions may be taken promptly to prevent the recurrence of the failure.[19]

At the heart of Failure Reporting System is a control organization that oversees implementation. Failure Reporting System also involves the use of a format and database that is used at all levels, throughout the project. Failure Reporting System should be initiated at the start of development and be continued until the project ends.

The implementation of Failure Reporting System is shown in Figure 7.

---

[17]Aeronautic Division of Wright-Patterson AFB. *Generic Integrated Maintenance Diagnostics (GIMADS) Task 12.* Draft of February 19, 1990, p. D-438.

[18]Department of the Navy. *Best Practices—How to Avoid Surprises in the World's Most Complicated Technical Process.* Washington DC; NAVSO P-6071, U.S. Government Printing Office, March 1986, p. 5-10.

[19]Some of the literature uses "corrective modification" as a synonym for "corrective action" or "remedial action."

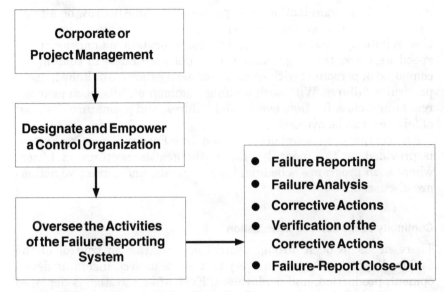

Figure 7 Implementation of a Failure Reporting System.

Designate a control organization

Corporate or Project Management needs to designate a control organization in the Failure Reporting System for assessing failures and directing corrective actions. This organization may have any of a number of names, of which some are:

- Failure Review Board
- Quality Assurance
- Product Integrity
- Reliability and Maintainability

More than one of these names might apply during the duration of a project, e.g. the Failure Review Board during development testing, and Quality Assurance during manufacturing. However, if more than one of these organizations is working on a project, only one organization should have responsibility for control. If two or more organizations share this responsibility, problems are likely to arise. For example, failures may occur for which neither organization feels responsible. When this happens, the failure or its remediation will not be pursued.

The control organization for the Failure Reporting System plays a key role; without a strong central control organization, activities may not be focused and controlled enough to achieve system requirements. The control organization must have the authority and resources to conduct and direct Failure Reporting System activities thoroughly and promptly. This organization must possess or be able to draw on all necessary project disciplines, such as systems engineering, design, logistics, reliability, manufacturing, and configuration management. To speed its work, this organization may delegate tasks to committees composed of personnel with specific technical expertise or knowledge of particular failures. With such staffing, common pitfalls, such as incorrect failure classification, overlooked failures, and premature close-out of failures, can be avoided.

An example of a control organization for a Failure Reporting System is provided by the monthly state-of-the-health meetings at Litton, where each program's schedule, failure trends, and corrective actions are discussed.[20]

Continuity of the control organization

There needs to be a strong, central organization in control of the Failure Reporting System in every phase of a project, including development, production, and deployment. Even after a system is deployed in the field, failures will emerge that need analysis and require redesign and retesting.

If one organization controlling the Failure Reporting System hands off control to another organization, this handoff should be managed in a way that preserves the history of failure reports that have not yet been closed out.

Perform failure reporting system activities

After corporate or project management has set up a Failure Reporting System and has designated a central control organization, that organization ultimately is responsible for identifying and removing all causes of failure of the system hardware and software. These activities should extend beyond development into production, field testing, and end-user experience. This organization should coordinate the interactions of subcontractors with the Failure Reporting System. It also should ensure that all decision-makers receive reports on failure-analyses, engineering receives special reports, quality assurance gets trend reports, and management obtains summary and special reports. Figure 8 shows a typical Failure Reporting System with its control organization.[21]

---

[20]Best Manufacturing Practices. *Report of Survey Conducted at Litton Guidance and Guidance Systems Division.* Woodland Hills, CA: October 1985, p. 7.

[21]Adapted from AT&T Bell Laboratories. *Reliability by Design.* Indianapolis, IN: AT&T Customer Information Center, 1989, p. 125.

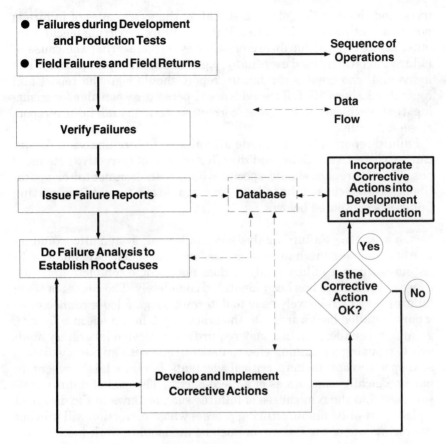

Figure 8 Closed-loop Failure Reporting System.

Failure verification. After documenting a failure, the tester should verify it by repeating the test or by obtaining and retaining physical evidence. A major risk in Failure Reporting System is that designers lose pertinent information because failed items (e.g., piece parts) are removed hastily or discarded. Instead, carefully removing and retaining failed items and recording their symptoms of failure makes it easier to confirm a repetition of an earlier failure and to find the root cause of multiple failures.

Failure reporting. Each failure or discrepancy occurring during testing should be reported and documented. A project-wide test-report format and database, of which examples are provided later, should be used. The failure report must identify the failed item, the failure symptoms, the conditions at the time of the failure, any indication from built-in tests, and the duration of the test. Often, the exact cause of failure is not known at the time of failure. But the failure-reporting mechanism must capture failed hardware or other evidence, so that the cause of failure can be identified eventually, e.g., during the repair process. The individual who creates the failure report should sign the report and route it together with failure evidence to persons responsible for ensuring that verification analysis, corrective action, and failure-report close-out occur.

Failure reports should include all failures, failure analyses, failure causes, corrective actions, and the effectiveness of corrective actions. If possible, the report should specify whether environmental or operational stresses caused the failure. An example of a format for reporting failures is presented below.

Failure analysis. Failure analysis is the logical, systematic examination of the modes, mechanisms, causes, and consequences of failures. In its purest form a failure analysis does not become complete until the cause of the failure has been identified completely. The causes of some failures may be relatively easy to determine, e.g., a loose connector or a part installed backwards. On the other hand, for an obscure failure, gaining this understanding may require sophisticated laboratory analysis (e.g., using a scanning electron microscope with an energy dispersive spectroscope to map critical elements [e.g., metals] present in microscopically small areas of a piece-part.[22]) The goal of failure analysis is to find the root causes of failures such as flaws in the design of a piece-part or its manufacturing process whose correction will prevent the recurrence of the failure, or such as inadequate work instructions causing assembly errors.

When a subsystem fails prior to system acceptance, the responsible party (e.g., the contractor producing the subsystem) has an obligation to help in determining the root cause of the failure. Other contractors should assist in this determination if their subsystems are involved. For example, weapon failures on a ship may involve hull, engine, and power-supply subsystems.

Corrective actions. Failure analysis should lead to changes in design, process, procedure, materials, or software to correct the cause of a failure or design deficiency. Developers should implement corrective actions

---

[22]Walsh, L., Wurster, R., and Kimber, R. J., Eds. *Quality Management Handbook.* New York: Marcel Dekker, ASQC Quality Press, 1986, pp. 571–618.

early, because recurrence of the failure can be costly, and because design changes, if needed, grow in cost as development continues.

Verification of the corrective action. After implementing a corrective action, the organization controlling the Failure Reporting System should monitor the system to ensure that the cause of failure has been eliminated and that no new problems have been introduced. If the corrective action proves ineffective, the failure report should stay open until tests have verified the effectiveness of additional actions taken to eliminate the causes of this failure. Also, this organization needs to make certain that the correction is installed in all systems in the factory and in the field.

Failure-report close-out. A failure report can be closed out *after* a corrective action has remedied the cause of the failure. The control organization needs to monitor the age of every open failure report, to make sure that each is closed out before a preassigned deadline.

Choose and use a single test-result format and database. The organization controlling the Failure Reporting System needs to standardize on a single project-wide format and database for reporting the results of tests throughout each project. The improvement in understandability and accessibility that a single format and database can produce make it more likely that test results will lead to eliminating (or at least reducing) the causes of test failures.

Contractors sometimes express frustration about the system for reporting test results in their project. In one survey, 83 out of 97 contractors felt that the system they used for collecting diagnostic data was inadequate for their needs.[23] The majority of these contractors wanted improvements in the timeliness, amount, dissemination, types, accuracy, and detail of data. A single format and database can help achieve these things.

Designating a test-reporting format. The organization controlling the Failure Reporting System should specify the reporting format for all testing, including DT&E and OT&E. This organization should require also that all contractors and project management use this format for reporting test data, including failures.

---

[23]General Dynamics, Fort Worth Division. *Generic Integrated Maintenance Diagnostics (GIMADS) Task 12.* Fort Worth, TX: Draft of February 19, 1990, p. D-51.

The single format should include specifications of graphical methods for presenting test data. A graph of test data (ideally including confidence intervals), such as that in *Uniform Test Report,* can show whether system reliability (e.g., Mean Time Between Failures [MTBF]) is improving as testing progresses.[24]

Setting up a project-wide test-results database.   The organization controlling the Failure Reporting System should oversee the setting up of a standard, computerized database for recording test data, including all test failures. Using the standard format, contractors should submit test-failure reports to this organization for entry into the database. Any of the project's contractors should be able to query (but not be permitted to modify) this database from their own terminals or computers, to learn the status of any failure report entered previously.

Contractors should use this database to learn whether the symptoms of any previously recorded failure match the symptoms of the current failure. Software associated with the database should:

- Compute and plot statistics such as the Mean Time Between Failures (MTBF)

- Provide summaries and special reports for project management, designers, programmers, and manufacturing engineers

- Generate exception reports when a deadline for analyzing or correcting failures is missed

Examples of test-report formats.   Several test-result reporting formats in use at AT&T[25] appear in the next three figures, which contractors or the government can modify as required for a particular project. These formats need to be supplemented by formats for tags affixed to failed equipment returned for repair and failure-cause analysis.

Figure 9 provides an example of a form for reporting failures, including "failure indications" or "troubles."

Figure 10 is an example of a failure-analysis report form.

Figure 11 is an example of a form for summarizing the investigation and correction of the cause of failure.

---

[24]For a stated period of test time, the MTBF (or cumulative MTBF) is the duration of the stated period of time divided by the number of failures that occurred during the stated time.

[25]Adapted from Crow, L. H. and Robbins, N. B. *The AT&T-FSAT Handbook on Integrated Reliability-Growth Testing.* To be published.

FAILURE REPORT

General Information

System ID _____   Failure Report # _____

Repair Tags _____

Failure Indication Occurred   Failure Indication Cleared
        date _____   date _____
        time _____   time _____
  hour meter _____   hour meter _____

Originator Name _____

Failure Isolation

Operational Mode   Failure Class
  ____ normal   ____ totally inoperative
  ____ maintenance   ____ major function loss
  ____ standby   ____ degraded operation
  ____ power down   ____ other (explain)
  ____ other (explain)   _____
_____   _____

   Failure Description   Contributing Factors
_____   _____
_____   _____
_____   _____

Isolation Started   Isolation Ended
        date _____   date _____
        time _____   time _____
  hour meter _____   hour meter _____

Diagnostics/Techniques Used to Isolate Failure
_____
_____
_____

Provide information on back of form for each unit that is replaced or repaired

---

For FRB Use Only

MR # Assigned _____

Comments _____
_____

Figure 9 Example of a failure reporting form.

FAILURE-ANALYSIS REPORT

General Information

System ID _____   Trouble Report # _____

Engr(s) Assigned _____   # Repair Tags _____

Date _____   # Def-Part Tags _____

Multiple Part Failure Analysis

Dependent Parts Failing

1. _____   4. _____
2. _____   5. _____
3. _____   6. _____

Cause of Multiple Failure

_____
_____
_____

Independent Parts Failing

1. _____
2. _____
3. _____

Design Analysis

_____
_____
_____
_____
_____
_____

Recommendations for Corrective Action

_____
_____
_____
_____
_____

Analysis Completed

Name _____   Date _____

Figure 10 Example of a failure-analysis report form.

FAILURE-REVIEW-BOARD SUMMARY REPORT

General Information

System ID _____   Trouble Report # _____

Date _____   MR # Assigned _____

Data and Analysis Review

Form(s)	Received	Reviewed	Initials
Failure Report			
Repair Tags (all)			
Defective Part Tags (all)			
Environmental Log			
Operational Log			
Failure Analysis Report			

Failure Determination

Cause of Failure _____

Relevant Failure _____   Nonrelevant Failure _____

Criteria _____

MTTF Chargeable Failure _____

Criteria _____

Corrective Action Determination

Corrective Action		Action Implemented	
None Taken	_____	Date	_____
Immediate Action	_____	Hour Meter	_____
Delayed Action	_____	Action effectiveness verified	_____

Criteria _____   Comments _____

Authorized by _____   Date _____

Figure 11 Example of a failure-report closeout form.

Design Limit

Design-limit testing otherwise known as environmental qualification testing ensures that the system or subsystem performs according to specification when exposed to "worst case" environments expected throughout the overall life cycle of the system. This testing forces improved system design if the system falls short of specifications.

Design-limit tests usually subject the system to extremes of temperature, vibration, humidity, salinity, pressure, voltage, or shock. Sometimes extreme stresses occur together during the mission, and design-limit tests must check system performance during these concurrent stresses. For example, high humidity and high temperature often occur together, as do low pressure and low temperature.

Because different systems have different missions, design-limit tests vary from system to system and must be based individually on each mission profile.

Introduction

Often the real environment a system or component faces is more severe than the system's nominal environment. For example, heat generated collectively by electronic elements of a computer may cause temperature stress on an element, e.g., an electronic chip, that far exceeds the ambient temperature of the computer's environment.

Sometimes laboratory test environments fail to represent worst-case environments, making it hard to test the design limit of a system.

Usually, the design-limit environment is not the worst environment that the system can tolerate. I.e., the system has design margin that enables it to survive in even worse environments. Ultimately, these environmental stresses will destroy the system or degrade its performance to unacceptable levels.

Sometimes developers push system testing beyond the design-limit or worst-case environment until the system breaks or gives unacceptable performance. That testing shows the safety zone or "design margin" by which system capability exceeds the predicted worst-case mission environments.

Figure 12 shows a schematic of these definitions.

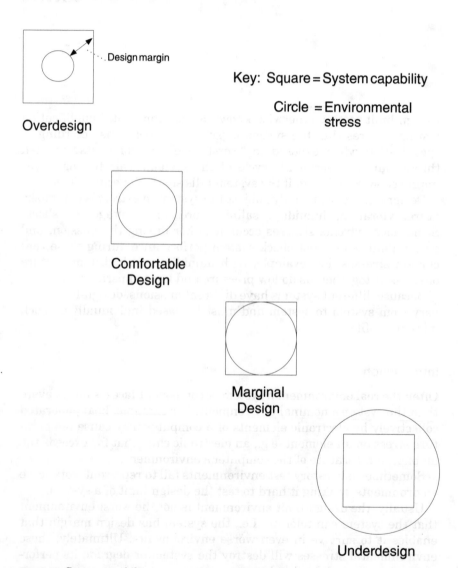

Figure 12 System capability versus environmental stress.

Benefits of design-limit testing

Design-limit testing provides the following benefits:

- Equipment designs handle "worst case" life-cycle environments.
- Test environments represent system and subsystem life-cycle environments.
- Equipment will survive the extremes of life-cycle environments.

Figure 13 illustrates the design-limit testing process.

Risks and Their Consequences

Table 3 summarizes the risks and consequences prevented by Design Limit testing.

Risk: Tests do not represent worst-case operating environments

When test environments fail to represent worst-case life-cycle profile environments, the test results do not represent system performance during worst-case conditions. Thus, users do not get a true picture of system reliability under severe environmental conditions.

If necessary, test conditions should be extended beyond those specified in military standards and system specifications. Test conditions should include environments derived from the mission profile. Any environment other than the mission-profile may result in unknown system performance and reliability.

System mission profiles must define the test environment or the worst-case environment for subsystems and system-related equipment, such as system test equipment for the field.

Risk: In-service equipment takes a new role without additional testing

When in-service equipment is used in a new role or application, mission strategists must compare the new mission environment with the old. If the environments differ, the equipment may need retesting and modification.

Risk: Support equipment not tested at worst-case

The mission environment may place more severe strain on related equipment than on the main system. To avoid support-equipment fail-

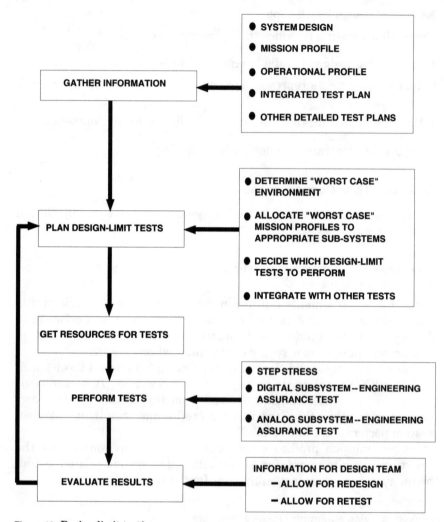

Figure 13 Design-limit testing.

ures during the mission, test environments must be specified for all equipment, not just the main system. For example, equipment used to continually test the system may suffer from exposure to heat, cold, or humidity.

Risk: Earlier design-limit tests substitute for new operating environments

Design-limit measurement relates directly to the mission-profile environment. Any changes in environmental conditions of the life-cycle pro-

TABLE 3   Risks and Consequences Addressed by Design-Limit Testing

Risks	Consequences
Tests do not represent worst-case operating environments	Inadequate design margins cause failures
	System performance in new operating environments is doubtful because its performance is unknown in the mission-profile environment
In-service equipment takes a new role without additional testing	System fails during operation, jeopardizing lives and mission success
Support equipment not tested in worst-case environment	Support equipment fails in the field
Earlier design-limit tests substitute for new operating environments	Design does not tolerate the new operating environment

file should automatically result in comparing old and new environments and in careful review of previous test procedures and results.

Procedures

This chapter describes high-level procedures for design-limit testing. These procedures ensure that system or subsystem designs meet performance requirements when exposed to worst-case environments of the life-cycle mission profile. Worst-case environmental conditions are the worst stresses the system experiences during its life. Beyond the design limit, operability of the system is uncertain.

Gather information

The information needed for design-limit testing is as follows:

- System design requirements
- Life cycle
- Integrated Test Plan
- Other detailed test plans

System design. Prior to design-limit testing, complete design documentation provides a path of communication between the design engineer and the test engineer who conducts the test.

Design documentation also includes information on part screens, possible failure modes, and the stress tolerance of parts under various environmental conditions.

Life-cycle mission profile. Testers should determine the life-cycle history of the system from factory acceptance throughout its useful life. The life-cycle description includes: handling, shipping, and storage prior to use; time between missions, e.g., stand-by or storage or transfer to and from repair sites; geographical locations of expected deployment; and platform environments.

Planners of design-limit tests must describe all potential deployment scenarios and take into account the following:

- Configuration of the hardware
- Platforms with which the hardware will interface
- Interfaces with other equipment
- Geographical locations
- Operating environments
- Probability of environmental conditions
- Duration of exposure phases
- Number of times phases occur
- Any other information that will help identify any environmental conditions which may act upon the item

More information on mission profile can be found in *Design to Reduce Technical Risk.*

Integrated test. Integrated test should include design-limit testing and ensure that all design-limit tests are properly scheduled with adequate resources available. An integrated test plan can prevent:

- Schedule slippage
- Omission of tests
- Duplication of tests
- Conflicts between test schedule and test design
- Ineffective use of resources and equipment

See the chapter on integrated test in this part for more information.

Plan design-limit tests. Planners of design-limit tests should:

- Determine worst-case environment
- Allocate worst-case mission-profile conditions to subsystems
- Decide which design-limit tests to perform

■ Integrate with other tests

Determine worst-case environment.   Based on the life cycle of events and environmental conditions, the planners of design-limit tests can determine the worst-case environment. The worst case is a stress condition that has the most adverse effect on the system. The following are common stresses on systems:

■ Electrical

■ Thermal

■ Thermal shock

■ Mechanical

■ Vibrational

■ Chemical (e.g., solvent effect)

■ Salt fog

■ Humidity

■ Altitude

■ Pressure

A system may experience one stress or a combination of several stresses. Designers of design-limit tests should plan tests that determine the effect of each extreme stress on the system and combinations of stresses. Typically, worst-case conditions are formed by a combination of several stresses.

Allocate worst-case mission profile to appropriate subsystems.   Subsystems should be tested under appropriate worst-case stresses. Although subsystems are part of the whole system, their stress levels may differ from those of the whole system. In such cases, the design-limit stress levels should be determined separately. As an example, the interior of a television is warmer than the cabinet of the television. To test temperature effects on an internal subsystem, planners determine the worst-case temperature that the subsystem experiences and use that temperature in design-limit testing.

Decide which design-limit test to perform.   Tests of a system or subsystem should match the mission profile. After determining the appropriate stresses and their operating levels, testers should perform the design-limit testing either in a single-stress application test or using a combination of stresses.

Integrate with other tests. As part of integrated test, test planners should integrate design-limit tests with other tests to avoid schedule slippage, duplication of tests, and unnecessary delays in the design-improvement process. In particular, planners should integrate design-limit tests with reliability-growth tests and life tests.

Get resources for tests

For design-limit testing, prototype samples that represent final manufacturing products should be tested. The prototype samples should be built as early as possible and tested at an early stage of design development. However, it is best to build prototypes using production equipment if possible. Early prototyping allows designers to eliminate design deficiencies at the system development stage and avoid costly failures later in the system's life-cycle.

Depending on the type of testing and environmental conditions, select the test procedure. Identify whether the test should be a combined environment test or a series of single tests. After identifying the appropriate test, order the proper equipment. All instrumentation should meet the accuracy needs of the test, and that accuracy should be verified before and after each test.

Engineering assurance testing. The Engineering Assurance Tests (EATs)[26] are tests conducted by engineering to validate the design of a system against the design limits of the specifications.

EATs are normally conducted at the Functional Item Replacement (FIR) level. In addition to testing the design against the specific limits and requirements, EATs go beyond the limits to measure the robustness of the design. The complexity of the design determines the number and extent of EATs to be performed.

EATs include but are not limited to the following:

- Electrical operation at and beyond maximum limits
- Dynamic range limits
- Gain and phase limits and channel-to-channel variations
- Electronic noise
- Specified Electromagnetic Interference (EMI) limits
- Power-supply current-and-ripple rejection
- Common-mode rejection

---

[26]Muchlinski, D. A., Hughes Aircraft Company, Fullerton, CA: March 1991, Private Communication.

- Over-current protection
- Transient response
- HV breakdown
- Low-voltage dropout
- Electrical isolation
- Thermal measurements to verify thermal analysis
- Manufacturing screening levels
- Compatibility with existing system hardware and software
- Mechanical interchangeability

Evaluate results

In any design-limit test, testers should record and provide information to the design team for their redesign efforts. This information is summarized in Table 4.[27]

After the redesign efforts and corrective actions, the system should be retested to find out:

- Whether the particular failure mode was eliminated
- Whether any new failure mode was introduced
- Whether the new system design is fault free

TABLE 4   Design-Limit Information Needed by the Design Team

1. Identification of test item and the individual test plan
2. Pretest, during-test, and post-test performance data
3. Test cycle, including environmental conditions applied
4. History of each failure occurrence
5. Nature of failure, including environmental effects
6. Temperature
7. Type, location, and orientation of stress-measuring sensors
8. Description and calibration status of data recorders and data analyzers
9. Voltage modulation applied during the mission-simulation portion of each test cycle
10. Frequency modulation applied during the mission-simulation portion of each test
11. Electrical stress induced by mission-related transients within the electrical system
12. Prior test history of test item
13. Corrective action proposed

---

[27]Military Standard 810E, *Environmental Test Methods and Engineering Guidelines*. Wright-Patterson AFB, OH, July 14, 1989.

5

Life

Life testing is testing that determines how long the system remains useful based on long-term exposure to the mission environments.

Tests ensure that the design will not fail prematurely from metal fatigue, corrosion, component aging, etc.

Delays in starting the tests, lack of feedback to the design process, and misunderstood acceleration factors have limited the benefits of life testing.

Introduction

Life testing assesses the adequacy and expected operational life of a system when it is exposed to mission-profile environments.

Because there is too little time during development to observe the natural death of a system having years of life expectancy, methods exist that speed up system aging. These so-called accelerated life tests allow testers to estimate years of life after a few days or months of testing. If the system survival estimate does not meet the requirements, changes will be made to assure that it will.

Accelerated life testing

In an accelerated life test, statistical methods are applied to the observed failures to estimate the life of a system under actual mission conditions. To accelerate the testing, systems or devices are subjected to stresses greater than those of normal mission conditions.

While performing accelerated life tests using high stress, the test engineer must avoid excessive or unrealistic conditions that cause failure modes that could not happen during a real mission. For example, engineers should not accelerate pressure aging by raising system pressure to levels that crush the system. Similarly, increasing temperature beyond a certain level may change a material's characteristics and negate any information obtained from the test.[28] The part's physical properties and an analysis of the observed failure modes will indicate whether the test itself initiated new failure modes.

An alternative test to the accelerated aging test is the aging test. In this test the system is exposed to its actual mission environment for an extended period of time. Because this method requires a substantial amount of time, the test should begin long before the end of full-scale development (FSD). If the required life span of the system is short, aging testing can be used. If the required life span is long (e.g., many years), accelerated aging testing must be used.

Keys to success

Unless a proven acceleration factor is available, accelerated life testing will not estimate the life of the system accurately.

Life testing should consider a realistic life-cycle mission profile that includes the worst case mission profile.

The program budget must include resources for life testing and the analysis of test results. The integrated test plan must describe in detail how to perform tests and analyses and how the results will impact the design process.[29]

Analysis, accelerated aging tests, or aging tests can verify the system's capability to operate over its required lifetime. Risk is inevitable if the analysis overlooks any failure mode or if the aging tests are not properly defined for the system.

Risks and Their Consequences

Table 5 summarizes the risks and consequences avoided by life testing.

Risk: Life tests are done late in the acquisition process

The life expectancy of the system depends on its design. To achieve the desired level of life expectancy, testers must do life testing as soon as equipment representative of the final design is available. In this way

---

[28]Priest, J. W. *Engineering Design For Producibility and Reliability.* New York: Marcel Dekker, 1988, pp. 164–165.

[29]Raytheon. *Transition from Development to Production: Management Manual,* Document 956010, February 1985.

TABLE 5 **Risks and Consequences Addressed by Life Testing**

Risks	Consequences
Life tests are done late in the acquisition process	System design is deficient Redesign is costly
Life test environments do not match mission profiles	System will experience unexpected failure mechanisms during operational use
Unknown, misunderstood, or wrong accelerated-testing techniques are used	Unrealistic life projections cause overdesign or underdesign
Results of life tests are not provided to system engineers	System life expectancy cannot be predicted accurately
Analysis of life uses only existing data from previous system	Life tests not tailored to the new or redesigned system will result in an unreliable system

designers can eliminate deficiencies of system design and make necessary improvements early in the development phase.

Risk: Life test environments do not match mission profiles

Life testing measures the effect of test environments on system design and life expectancy of the system. If the test environment does not include the actual mission environment, the life estimate cannot be reliable.

Risk: Unknown or faulty accelerated-testing techniques are used

Test planners must use known, valid accelerated-life techniques. Otherwise, estimates of the system's life expectancy and performance will be unreliable.

Because the acceleration factor determines the relationship between the failure rate of a system under the test conditions and mission life, it is essential to know the nature of this parameter; otherwise, the life expectancy of the system is uncertain.

Risk: Results of life tests are not provided to systems engineers

Life-test results must be quickly provided to system engineers. Delay hinders improvement of the system design and result in unexpected failures during the mission.

Risk: Analysis of life uses only existing data from previous system

Existing data on an old system will be helpful if its mission-profile environment and design components were similar to those of the system under the test. Otherwise, test engineers should design a new life test based on the new mission profile in order to find all potential failure mechanisms in the new environment.

Procedures

Life testing assesses the life expectancy of the equipment design operating in life-cycle environments. A common technique for evaluating the life expectancy of a system is accelerated life testing.

Benefits

The benefits of determining the life expectancy of a system are:

- System performance sustained throughout its life
- More-accurate maintenance and support planning
- Realistic simulation of system aging characteristics
- Fewer failures

Accelerated life testing

Testers use accelerated life testing to get information quickly on the life expectancy of products and materials. Such testing subjects the system to conditions that are more severe than normal conditions. Accelerated tests typically expose systems to high temperature, voltage, pressure, vibration, cycling rate, load, etc., or combinations of these conditions. The use of certain accelerating or stress variables is a well-established engineering practice for many products and materials.

Analysts use the data obtained at the accelerated conditions and a model to determine the life expectancy of a system under normal conditions. Such testing saves time and cost compared with testing at normal conditions. Indeed, for many products and materials, life testing at normal conditions is impossible.

Prior to life testing, engineers should survey statistical methods for planning and analyzing accelerated tests. This will allow them to:

- terminate a test before all units fail
- test at lower stress to reduce extrapolation uncertainty
- save time and cost

Figure 14 shows a schematic of accelerated life testing.

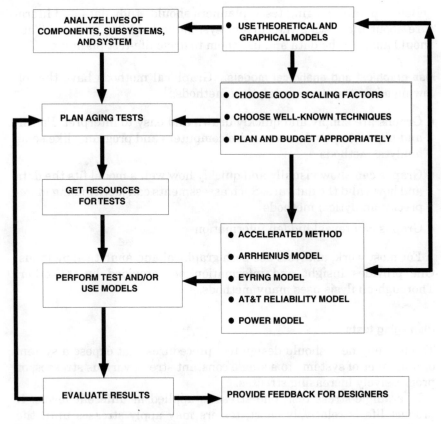

Figure 14 Accelerated life testing.

Analyze system life expectancy

Before scheduling an accelerated life test, planners should know the effects of environment on the failure mechanisms.

Various models help planners understand how stress levels determine the most likely failure modes and failure rates. Experience shows that a model that works well for one component or system may poorly predict failure of others. Thus analysts must align life-expectancy models with component, subsystem, and system materials. For example, the "power rule" model is best for paper capacitors, whereas the "Arrhenius" and "Eyring" models best fit semiconductors.[30]

---

[30]Priest, J. W. *Engineering Design for Producibility and Reliability.* New York: Marcel Dekker, 1988, p. 164.

Before planning aging tests, planners should study data and literature about life testing the current system and similar systems. They should analyze the data and use them to drive life-test planning.

Use graphical and analytical models. Graphical methods have the following advantages over analytical methods:[31]

- Graphs are simply and quickly drawn and easy to interpret. Pencil-and-paper graphs do not require computers and programs like some analytic methods
- Graphs can show visually and quickly how well a model fits the data and how valid the data are. Such assessments can justify using more-precise analytical methods
- Graphs can reveal hidden information

For most work, analysts use both graphical and analytical methods. One provides insight and information not provided by the other. Thorough analysis uses many methods.

Plan aging tests

The test engineer should design test procedures that expose a system or a number of systems to a single constant stress, various stresses, or progressively increasing stresses.

In a single-stress test, one stress is applied at different levels. If product life is relatively short, testers may apply stresses until the product fails. In a more aggressive method, testers apply a high stress level until the product fails. This method shortens times to failure, but analysis becomes more difficult.

To plan aging tests, planners should choose well-known techniques.

Scaling factors. Scaling factors are multipliers that convert the duration of an accelerated test to equivalent mission life.

For example, if the scaling factor is 500, the system will take 500 times longer under normal operation to manifest a failure mode than under accelerated conditions. In other words, one hour at the accelerated condition equals 500 hours at the normal mission conditions.

Life-expectancy analysts use different methods of calculating scaling factors for different systems. For example the Arrhenius scaling factor applies to temperature-accelerated tests in which product failure

---

[31]Nelson, W. *Accelerated Testing*. New York: John Wiley & Sons, 1990, pp. 113–145.

results from chemical degradation or intermetallic diffusion. Use the Arrhenius scaling factor for:

- Electrical insulators
- Solid-state and semiconductor devices
- Battery cells
- Lubricants and other greases
- Plastics
- Incandescent-lamp filaments

Variants of the Arrhenius scaling factor suit different products: the "Arrhenius-Weibull Model" fits capacitor dielectrics and insulating tape, while the "Arrhenius Exponential Model" fits semiconductors.

The Inverse Power Law or Power Law scales product life for:

- Electrical insulations and dielectrics in voltage-endurance tests
- Ball and roller bearings
- Incandescent lamps
- Flash lamps
- Metal fatigue due to mechanical loading or thermal cycling

The Power Log-Normal model gives the scaling factor for metal fatigue.

The Power Exponential model is a special case of the "Power-Weibull" model that provides a good fit for the life expectancy of transformer oil and certain semiconductors after burn-in.

Plan and budget appropriately. Planners of life tests should plan tests carefully to prevent schedule slippage and delays in design improvement. For example, in some cases the life test should last several years, and life testing should begin as soon as a representative final product is available, even if development efforts are continuing. That extended period of test time requires a budget for laboratory time and human resources.

Life testers may need several test specimens to accurately estimate the life or median life at design stresses.

Get resources for tests

Part or system selection for life testing is similar to that of design-limit testing. One difference is the time requirement. Because life testing lasts much longer than design-limit testing, it is essential to get the parts as soon as possible. In some cases, prior to the completion of the design process, a representative production sample (prototype) has to be made for life testing, so that designers have the results of testing to use in enhance design development.

Perform tests

Testers follow the life-testing schedule as time and resources permit.

The life-test plans should include estimates of test duration and should encourage testers to report early or unexpected failures to analysts and designers. Early failure may show the need for major design changes that should begin quickly.

Evaluate results

As with design-limit test results, testers should evaluate the results of life testing and report appropriate feedback to design engineers. The important element in this feedback process is time. For expediency, life testers should evaluate the life data as soon as possible so that the design engineers can make appropriate changes in the system design within the development schedule.

6

Test, Analyze, and Fix (TAAF)

Reliability is the ability of a system to operate under specified conditions for a stated period of time. Reliability is measured by metrics such as Mean Time Between Failures (MTBF), whose definition is: "For a stated period of test time, MTBF is the length of the stated period of time divided by the number of failures during the stated time."[32]

"Reliability testing" typically involves exercising a system in a manner simulating normal use. During this testing, failures are detected and recorded, along with the times at which these failures occur.

"Reliability requirements" are numerical specifications for the rate of failures observed during reliability testing. The contract for a government system generally contains reliability requirements.

Introduction

Although the words may suggest a broader meaning, *Test, Analyze, and Fix (TAAF)* has become identified with a program for achieving reliability growth, primarily during full-scale engineering development.[33] [34] [35] (The phrases "reliability development" and "reliability improvement" mean the same as "reliability growth.") In a successful reliability-growth program, system reliability improves until it meets or exceeds reliability requirements.

---

[32] Institute of Reliability Sciences (IES). *Glossary of Reliability Growth Terms.* 1989.

[33] Patterson, Douglas O., "The Navy and Reliability Growth: A Paradox At Best." *ITEA Journal,* Vol. 9(3), 1988, pp. 27–31.

[34] Department of Defense. *MIL-STD-785B, Reliability Program for Systems and Equipment Development and Production.* Washington, DC: DoD, September 15, 1980, task 302.

[35] Departments of the Air Force, Army, and Navy. *The TAAF Process, A Technical Brief for TAAF Implementation,* Washington, DC: HQ USAF, LE-RD; HQ AMC, QA; and OASN, S&L; January 1989, p. 2.

In a reliability-growth program, reliability improves primarily by modifying the design to eliminate modes of all failures observed during reliability testing, which in this context is called reliability-growth testing. After test analysts examine these failures to determine their causes, designers modify the hardware, software, or manufacturing process for the system to eliminate these specific, individual causes, so that these failures will not recur (or at least will be less likely to recur).[36]

Reliability-growth monitoring

A reliability-growth program includes the monitoring of the system's progress towards achieving its reliability objectives. In the early 1960's, J. T. Duane observed that the cumulative number of failures N(T) divided by the cumulative test time T was decreasing and fell close to a straight line when N(T) was plotted against T on log-log graph paper.[37] Duane's empirical observation applied to MTBF, also, except that both the cumulative and the instantaneous MTBF tended to follow a *rising* straight line when plotted on log-log graph paper. This "Duane postulate" is the most commonly accepted pattern for reliability growth and is reflected in both the Duane and the Crow (AMSAA) procedures (or "models") for measuring reliability.[38] [39] [40]

Figure 15 shows a reliability-growth curve like the one Duane observed.[41] The estimates of MTBF appear as data points connected by the line segments. This is a log-log plot, i.e., the horizontal and vertical scales are logarithmic. The dotted, rising, straight line illustrates the growth patterns for both the Duane and Crow (AMSAA) procedures for measuring reliability.

Reliability-growth programs

Historically, developers relied on reliability demonstration (or qualification) testing to prove that the system had met its reliability require-

---

[36]Department of Defense. *The TAAF Process, A Technical Brief for TAAF Implementation,* Washington, DC: HQ USAF, LE-RD; HQ AMC, QA; and OASN, S&L; January 1989, p. A-1.

[37]Duane, J. T. "Learning Curve Approach to Reliability Monitoring." *IEEE Transactions on Aerospace,* vol. 2, 1964, pp. 563–566.

[38]Crow, L. H. "New International Standards on Reliability Growth." *1991 Proceedings Annual Reliability and Maintainability Symposium,* 1991, pp. 478–480.

[39]Institute of Reliability Sciences (IES). *Glossary of Reliability Growth Terms.* Mount Prospect, IL: Institute of Environmental Sciences, 1989.

[40]"AMSAA" is the acronym for "Army Materiel Systems Analysis Agency."

[41]Duane, J. T. "Learning Curve Approach to Reliability Monitoring." *IEEE Transactions on Aerospace,* vol. 2, 1964, pp. 563–566.

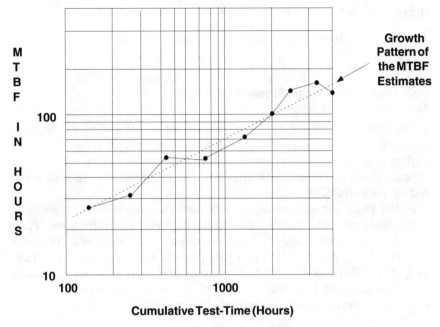

Figure 15 Example of the Duane model for reliability growth.

ment. Reliability demonstration testing is a non-productive cost and schedule driver and is not directed toward reliability improvement.

Programs of reliability-growth testing can minimize this risk. If properly managed, such programs include time for performance monitoring, failure detection, failure analysis, and the verification that design corrections work as expected.

Reliability-growth testing can be either "integrated" or "dedicated" (or a mixture of these two types). *Dedicated* reliability-growth testing is reliability-growth testing that:

- is run separately from other testing
- occurs on equipment dedicated to this testing throughout the period of dedicated testing

Typically, dedicated reliability-growth testing occurs during an isolated phase of the development process. During this phase, the system is tested under controlled conditions *solely* to achieve reliability growth through failure detection and corrective modifications.

Integrated reliability-growth testing is reliability-growth testing performed simultaneously with other development testing such as safety testing, environmental testing, or functional testing of a prototype system. This type of testing usually starts earlier and often lasts longer than the dedicated type.

Risks Avoided by TAAF

Table 6 summarizes the risks and consequences that can be avoided by using TAAF fully.

Risk: Only a reliability qualification (or demonstration) test is used

By definition, a reliability qualification test or reliability demonstration test evaluates the reliability of a system at the end of development. Unfortunately, such tests carry with them the risk of discovering significant design or manufacturing flaws too late to avoid expensive corrections of reliability problems.

In the past, project managers assumed that *predicted* estimates of reliability matched *actual* reliability during system development. They assumed they could verify the achievement of reliability requirements by a reliability qualification test just prior to manufacture. Unfortunately, this leaves too little time to remedy problems this testing uncovers. This approach may work if none of the technology used in the system's piece parts is new or state-of-the-art. But if any of the system's

---

TABLE 6   Risks and Consequences Prevented by TAAF

Risks	Consequences
Only a reliability qualification (or demonstration) test is used	The system may not satisfy reliability requirements
	End-of-development reliability problems may force expensive redesign of the system and its manufacture
Only *dedicated* reliability-growth testing is performed	The dedicated reliability-growth tests unnecessarily duplicate other tests, wasting time and money
	Corrective actions are late in the development program and are generally more expensive
Reliability improvements are not made quickly	Schedule slips, and increased costs result from changing designs, retooling the production line, and renegotiating purchasing arrangements
Reliability is improved only by adding redundancy	Although mission reliability will improve, neither the frequency of hardware failures nor the system's maintainability will improve
Estimates of current reliability do not reflect delayed fixes properly	An optimistic (or, rarely, pessimistic) view of the status of system reliability results
Reliability growth stops at the end of development (and TAAF)	Some failure modes may not appear until the system is in the field, which can threaten the mission and increase maintenance costs

technology is new, project management takes a very high risk if it fails to perform reliability tests and to use reliability-growth procedures as early as possible during development. The longer reliability growth is deferred, the greater the expense and time required for correcting reliability problems.

Risk: Only dedicated reliability-growth testing is performed

Running simultaneously with other development tests, *integrated* reliability-growth tests can save time and cost less than *dedicated* reliability-growth tests, which—although easier to administer—require allocating test time and equipment exclusively for this testing. (These two types were defined in a previous chapter.) Not using integrated reliability-growth testing—where appropriate—can waste time and money.

Risk: Reliability improvements are not made quickly

All too often, a corrective action does not remove the cause of failure, or it may cause another problem unexpectedly. If such reliability improvements are not designed and tested quickly (e.g., by off-line testing, if system test facilities are unavailable), there may be too little time to verify the effectiveness of those improvements and to make further corrections, if necessary.

Delays in verifying and implementing fixes for reliability problems often force schedule slips, redesign, retooling, and the renegotiation of purchasing arrangements. These changes may delay system delivery and generally cost more than they would if developers made the same changes early.

Risk: Reliability is improved only by adding redundancy

A standard way of improving system reliability is by modifying its architecture by adding redundancy, e.g., with a duplicate, parallel subsystem that takes over if the first subsystem fails. While this increases the probability that the system will be able to perform its mission properly, it should not substitute for reducing the failure rate of elements of the system by identifying and removing the causes of failure. The primary purpose of a reliability-growth program is to reduce the failure rate in this way, so that maintenance costs will decrease and the mean time between unscheduled maintenance actions (MTBUMA) will increase; if MTBUMA is made to increase, the mean time between failures (MTBF) for mission failures will increase, also.

The converse is *not* true: While adding redundancy improves MTBF for mission failures, it decreases MTBUMA. The reason for this can be understood from the example of the Blackhawk Helicopter: Its second engine increases the mission MTBF by improving the probability that the helicopter will be able to fly its missions successfully. But the second engine sometimes breaks down, which decreases MTBUMA. Besides reducing MTBUMA, adding redundancy may be impractical: If enough more engines were added to the Blackhawk Helicopter that it almost never would suffer a loss of power in flight, the helicopter also would not be able to meet its design requirements for weight, cost, performance, range, or size.

Risk: Estimates of current reliability do not reflect delayed fixes properly

Corrective actions often take substantial amounts of time to design and implement. When this delay between finding and fixing failure causes leads to installing system modifications between phases of reliability-growth testing, these modifications are called "delayed fixes," as in Figure 16.[42]

In estimating current reliability, it is necessary to take delayed fixes into account.[43] If not treated properly, delayed fixes can lead to an optimistic (or, rarely, pessimistic) view of the current status of the reliability program.

Risk: Reliability growth stops at the end of development (and TAAF)

It is mistaken economy to stop improving reliability once the system reaches the field, because some failure modes may not appear until then. Left vulnerable to those modes, the system may fail its mission and have increased maintenance costs. In military procurement, the causes of field failures may not be corrected unless a contract modification is issued to correct problems found after user acceptance tests.

TAAF can continue after development ends. For example, a post-development Product Improvement Program (PIP) caused the reliability of the Blackhawk Helicopter to increase well beyond initial requirements. TAAF can be continued by making the project office responsible for extending it into the field.

---

[42]*MIL-HDBK-189, Military Handbook, Reliability Growth Management.* Washington, DC: DoD, February 13, 1981.

[43]Crow, L. H. "Reliability Growth Projection From Delayed Fixes." *1983 Proceedings, Annual Reliability and Maintainability Symposium,* 1983, pp. 84–89.

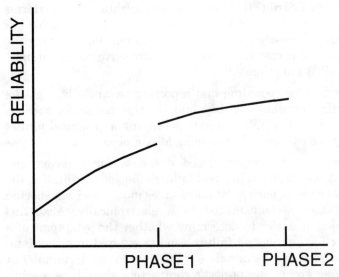

Figure 16 Reliability-growth curve with delayed fixes.

Procedures

The steps in a TAAF reliability-growth program are:

- Plan for reliability-growth testing
- Perform testing, analyze results, and correct the causes of failures
- Track reliability and compare with requirements

An effective reliability-growth program will include all of these steps.

Plan for reliability-growth testing

To prepare for reliability-growth testing, project management needs to set up a Failure Reporting System. Then it needs to make assessments and predictions of reliability and the need for a formal reliability-growth program. Finally, environmental-stress screening needs to be done.

Set up a failure reporting system, including an FRB. The cornerstone of an effective reliability-growth program is the establishment of a strongly managed and well-funded Failure-Reporting, Analysis, and Corrective Action System (FRACAS).[44] [45] In setting up the Failure Reporting System, project management needs to create:

---

[44]In this book, this is called the Failure Reporting System template.

[45]Department of Defense. *MIL-STD-2155(AS), Military Standard, Failure Reporting, Analysis, and Corrective Action System.* Washington, DC: DoD, July 24, 1985.

- a Failure Review Board (FRB)—or other organization that performs an equivalent function—that is *empowered* and *responsible* for requiring failure investigations and analyses and for ensuring the implementation of corrective actions (or "corrective modifications," as they are called sometimes).[46]

- a uniform format for recording and reporting test results, e.g., the failure-reporting format described later in this template, and the *Uniform Test Report (UTR)* template specifying a graphical format for showing progress towards achieving MTBF objectives.

- a single, project-wide, computerized database for entering and retrieving test results, including test failures. Besides facilitating the sharing of test results, such a database saves money and can shorten schedules if data is transmitted to it electronically. Also, this database makes it easier to determine whether the symptoms of a problem match symptoms on failure reports entered into the database previously. Using terminals (or PCs emulating terminals) at their own sites, any of the project's contractors should, as a minimum, be able to query this database's information, e.g., the diagnosis and corrective actions for failure reports.

Predict "inherent" (or "design growth potential") reliability. At the beginning of the project, reliability engineers need to predict the inherent reliabilities of the subsystem or system that the proposed reliability-growth program is capable of achieving. "Inherent reliability" is defined as an upper bound on the reliability that can be achieved by the reliability-growth program, given:

- resources (funding and technological) available for reliability improvement
- system architecture
- agreements between the government and developers regarding design strategy
- piece-part reliabilities
- data on the testing and use of previous, similar systems

To provide a margin of safety, the new system's inherent-reliability predictions should be at least 25% greater than the corresponding reliability requirement specified at the outset of the project (e.g., in the

---

[46]Department of Defense. *MIL-STD-2155(AS), Military Standard, Failure Reporting, Analysis, and Corrective Action System*. Washington, DC: DoD, July 24, 1985, par. 4.3.

project's development contract).[47] If the prediction is not 25% greater, system designers should try to reconfigure the system (e.g., by changing piece-part technologies or by adding redundancy) to reach that threshold.

Predict initial reliability. For new-technology, state-of-the-art systems, the reliability at the start of prototype testing invariably will be below the inherent reliability of the system. The initial reliability of early prototypes of complex, new-technology systems is typically 15% to 50% of their inherent reliability, with electronic systems averaging about 30 percent.[48] If no corrective modifications are made during development to improve reliability, the system's reliability will remain at the low initial level (e.g., 30%) and will likely fall short of requirements and expectations. In order to plan for reliability growth, the initial system reliability needs to be estimated.[49]

Assess the need for a formal reliability-growth program. If the predictions of initial reliability of the system are well above reliability requirements, the project may not need a formal program of reliability-growth testing. But the project will still need a comprehensive Failure Reporting System that includes the monitoring of reliability to verify that the predictions of initial reliability were correct.

Select a reliability-growth rate. For both the Duane and the Crow (AMSAA) procedures for measuring reliability, the *growth rate* is the slope of the line (shown on Figure 15) calculated from the failure data. In the Figure 15 example, the slope is 0.5, and the equation of this line is

$$\log(\text{MTBF}) = 0.5 \log(\text{time}) + C$$

where C is a constant. Government publications suggest that 0.5 is the slope that should be selected, but Benton and Crow have shown that the median growth slope of historical data from a number of programs was 0.31, and growth slopes as low as 0.25 are not unusual.[50] A low-risk, off-the-shelf project that uses proven technology usually has a

---

[47]This 25% rule-of-thumb is contained in: Department of the Navy. *Best Practices: How to Avoid Surprises in the World's Most Complicated Technical Process.* NAVSO P-6071, March 1986, p. 5-42.

[48]Benton, A. W. and Crow, L. W. "Integrated Reliability Growth Testing," *1989 Proceedings, Annual Reliability and Maintainability Symposium,* 1989, pp. 160–166.

[49]Crow, L. H. "On the Initial System Reliability," *1986 Proceedings, Annual Reliability and Maintainability Symposium.*

[50]Benton, A. W. and Crow, L. H. "Integrated Reliability Growth Testing," *1989 Proceedings, Annual Reliability and Maintainability Symposium,* 1989, pp. 160–166.

lower growth slope than a high-risk, state-of-the-art project that uses new technology.

Predict the duration of reliability-growth testing. When predicting the time involved in reliability-growth testing, project management should take into account:

- predictions of initial reliability
- predictions of inherent (or design strategy) reliability
- predictions of the rate of growth of reliability
- downtime for maintenance, repair, and test setup
- waiting time for troubleshooting, failure analysis, and corrective modifications
- the delays involved in making corrective modifications

Do environmental-stress screening (ESS). Environmental-stress screening (ESS) is stress applied to a system's hardware to disclose latent manufacturing defects. *It is important to apply ESS to prototype equipment before it is subjected to reliability-growth testing.* Vibration and temperature cycling are the most frequently used stresses on the system or sub-system level, while pressure and humidity (including pressurized steam) often are used for piece parts such as integrated circuits. Raising the stress levels to values that approach (but do not exceed) the design limits of the hardware can accelerate failure of these latent manufacturing defects; MTBF should not be measured during such tests. The *Design to Reduce Technical Risk* book addresses ESS in detail.

**Perform testing, analyze results, and correct
the causes of failures**

Three kinds of reliability testing described previously often occur during different stages of development:

- Reliability qualification (or demonstration) testing occurs before a final stage of development, when the system is being qualified for production.
- Dedicated reliability-growth testing often takes place just before reliability qualification testing.
- Integrated reliability-growth testing can occur on prototype systems, before factory-produced hardware is available. Later in development, this testing also can coexist with functional testing, integration testing, safety testing, and environmental testing.

Record test results, including test failures. Contractors should record test data, including any failures, in the Failure Reporting System, using a Uniform Test Report (UTR) format and database.

Analyze failures and correct the system. Contractors improve reliability by analyzing failures to determine the root causes of failure. With this knowledge, they can modify the system to reduce the incidence of failures—*or even to eliminate them entirely*—by reducing or removing the causes of these failures. The importance of timely root-cause determination and corrective action cannot be overstated—this is the key to a successful TAAF program.

Make design and process improvements throughout testing. Removing the causes of test-revealed failure is not the only way to improve reliability. Improving manufacturing processes is another way. For example, robust-design experiments have reduced the number of solder crosses between adjacent lines on printed-circuit boards; a manufacturing-process improvement like this can increase yields and reliability simultaneously.[51] Redesigning the manufacturing process fundamentally, e.g., by carefully applying only the minimum amount of low-solids flux to circuit boards, can eliminate a process step: in this instance, the need to clean the board after soldering.[52] Simplifying a production process can improve the reliability of the product. The *Moving a Design into Production* book discusses continuous manufacturing improvement.

Track reliability and compare with requirements

An essential part of TAAF is estimating reliability at various times during reliability-growth testing, making reliability projections, comparing these projections with requirements, and taking appropriate action if these projections do not exceed requirements.

Classify reliability-growth failures. Reliability engineers should classify the failures that occur during system-level TAAF testing as either:[53] [54]

---

[51]Phadke, M. S. *Quality Engineering Using Robust Design*. Englewood Cliffs, NJ: Prentice Hall, 1989.

[52]Guth, L. A. "Applicability of Low-Solids Flux." *Proceedings of the Singapore-U.S. Seminar on Chlorofluorocarbons,* September 17–19, 1990.

[53]Department of Defense. *MIL-STD-781D, Reliability Testing for Engineering Development, Qualification, and Production*. Washington, DC: DoD, October 17, 1987.

[54]Crow, L. H. and Robbins, N. B. *The AT&T-FSAT Handbook on Integrated Reliability-Growth Testing*. To be published.

- Relevant and chargeable failures, including failures due to design, workmanship, intermittency, automatic shutdown, maintenance, wear-out, and piece-part failure.

- Not-relevant or not-chargeable failures, including failures due to improper system installation, operator error, error in test procedures, or overstress conditions in excess of design requirements.

Since the MTBF calculation uses only failures that are *both* relevant and chargeable, there is no need to determine whether a failure is "relevant" or "chargeable," if it is not both of these simultaneously.

Choose a procedure for measuring the growth in reliability. The reliability-growth curve plots a reliability statistic (such as MTBF) vs. cumulative test time (e.g., hours of reliability-growth testing), cumulative number of tests or trials (e.g., rounds), or calendar time (e.g., months).[55] Often, analysts plot these data on a log-log graph, as in Figure 15. This plotting procedure reflects either of the following procedures (or "models") for representing the growth of reliability: (Both of these procedures are based on the "Duane Postulate," described previously.)

- The Duane procedure, which estimates the location and slope of the dotted line in Figure 15 by using a least-squares or eyeball fit to the MTBF calculations. This does not provide a quantitative measure of whether the Duane postulate is appropriate for the failure data. Also, it does not provide confidence limits on the location and slope parameters, since it fits cumulative instead of independent data-points.

- The Crow (AMSAA) procedure (or "model") estimates the location and slope parameters of Figure 15 by explicitly taking into account the variability of the failure data. The Crow (AMSAA) procedure includes parameter estimation, confidence intervals, and goodness-of-fit tests.[56] [57] Currently, the Crow procedure includes reliability growth projections when corrective modifications are delayed.[58] [59]

---

[55]Department of Defense. *MIL-HDBK-189, Military Handbook, Reliability Growth Management.* Washington, DC: DoD, February 13, 1981, p. 17.

[56]Department of Defense. *MIL-HDBK-189, Military Handbook, Reliability Growth Management,* Washington, DC: DoD, February 13, 1981, pp. 131–134.

[57]Institute of Reliability Sciences (IES). *Glossary of Reliability Growth Terms.* Mount Prospect, IL: Institute of Environmental Sciences, 1989.

[58]Crow, L. H. "Reliability Growth Projection From Delayed Fixes." *1983 Proceedings, Annual Reliability and Maintainability Symposium,* 1983, pp. 84–89.

[59]Robbins, N. B. "Tracking Reliability Growth with Delayed Fixes." *1990 Proceedings—Institute of Environmental Sciences,* 1990, pp. 754–757.

The Duane procedure is deterministic in the sense that it does not take into account the variability of the data. The Crow (AMSAA) procedure assumes the same growth pattern as the Duane procedure but formulates the occurrence of failures as a statistical (nonhomogeneous Poisson) process.[60][61] The Crow (AMSAA) procedure should be used when the system's reliability requirements include confidence intervals.[62]

Determine the growth of reliability.   To assess reliability growth:

- Using the Duane procedure, calculate and plot reliability statistics such as the *cumulative* MTBF (defined previously) calculated at various times during testing, as illustrated by the points (connected by line segments) on Figure 16. Then the *instantaneous* MTBF is calculated and compared with reliability requirements.[63]

- For the Crow (AMSAA) procedure, use maximum likelihood estimates to calculate the parameters of the Duane pattern of reliability growth. The Crow (AMSAA) procedures also permit performing goodness-of-fit tests and calculating confidence intervals.[64]

Make reliability projections and compare with requirements.   During reliability-growth testing, it is essential to project reliability to the end of reliability-growth testing. This projection can be performed by applying an extension of the Crow procedure that includes statistically based formulas for projecting reliability after delayed fixes; this procedure has been accepted as an international standard.[65][66] After this projec-

---

[60]Crow, L. H. "Reliability Analysis for Complex Repairable Systems." Philadelphia, PA: *Reliability and Biometry,* Proshan, F. and Serfling, R. J., Eds., SIAM, 1974, pp. 379–410.

[61]Crow, L. H. "Estimation Procedures for the Duane Model." Aberdeen Proving Ground, MD: *Proceedings US AMSAA Reliability Growth Symposium,* September 1972.

[62]Crow, L. H. "Reliability Analysis for Complex Repairable Systems." Philadelphia, PA: *Reliability and Biometry,* Proshan, F. and Serfling, R. J., Eds., SIAM, 1974, pp. 379–410.

[63]Department of Defense. *MIL-STD-1635(EC), Reliability Growth Testing.* Washington, DC: DoD, February 3, 1978, pp. 18–20.

[64]Department of Defense. *MIL-HDBK-189, Military Handbook, Reliability Growth Management.* Washington, DC: DoD, February 13, 1981, pp. 131–134.

[65]Crow, L. H. "New International Standards on Reliability Growth." *1991 Proceedings Annual Reliability and Maintainability Symposium,* 1991, pp. 478–480.

[66]International Electrotechnical Commission. *Programs for Reliability Growth.* Geneva, Switzerland: International Standard CEI IEC 1014, 1st ed., 1989.

tion has been compared with the reliability requirement, appropriate actions can be taken, e.g., dedicating more resources to improving reliability, if the projection falls short of the requirement.

Continue reliability growth beyond end of testing.   The Failure Reporting System, with its Failure Review Board (or successor organization empowered by the government), should continue beyond the end of testing (and of TAAF):

- to oversee the elimination of previous causes of failures
- to track and resolve new failure causes appearing during manufacture, deployment, and use.
- to make sure that failures are analyzed and remedied quickly enough. Such monitoring of the cycle time from failure to corrective modification is a measure of the effectiveness of the Failure Reporting System.

Uniform Test Report

During development a variety of tests are performed to assess progress in meeting design requirements. The results of each test are presented individually, and an assessment is made concerning the achievement of the objectives of the particular test under review. Normally the format used to present these results at the project management level does not provide an indication of progress being made toward achieving overall reliability program requirements. The results presented only indicate the success or failure in passing a particular test.

To provide reliability trend analysis for management visibility it is essential that all test data be analyzed and displayed in a consistent manner.

Introduction

The *Uniform Test Report* template provides a Uniform Test Report format. Table 7 summarizes risks and their consequences if the formats of test reports are not uniform across a development project.

Risk: Contractors use different formats for reporting test data

If the prime contractor and all subcontractors do not all use the same format for reporting test data, the prime contractor cannot easily com-

TABLE 7　Risks and Consequences Addressed by Uniform Test Report

Risks	Consequences
Contractors use different formats for reporting test results	Test results are misinterpreted and are difficult to analyze
Test results are displayed in a poor format	Information is lost, and results are not used to track design maturity against contract requirements

pile and compare test data. Similarly, if contractors cannot access a common database, they cannot easily retrieve needed data. As a result, management will not have the visibility of the overall test program that it needs to assess design maturity. By monitoring test progress against contractual requirements, resources can be shifted to subsystems having design problems.

For example, in the Air Force's B-1B Bomber's central integrated test system, subcontractors reported data in different formats, which slowed progress.[67] Converting the data to a standard format corrected this problem.

Risk: Test results are displayed in a poor format

If test results are not displayed clearly, e.g., in a graphical format, it is difficult to compare these results with related design requirements. Large quantities of unsummarized test data may hide valuable insights about system reliability, failure causes, and performance shortfalls.

Procedures

Formal reliability-development tests using the Test Analyze and Fix (TAAF) method normally are performed for failure-mode identification and elimination. During these tests, all results are reported in a format that provides acquisition managers with visibility of actual versus predicted reliability growth. Results from other tests being performed during the development and transition phases usually are reported in different formats. This change in format precludes merger of test results and prevents an overall assessment of design maturity by acquisition managers.

Contractors sometimes express frustration about the system for reporting test results in their project. In one survey, 83 out of 97 contractors felt that the system they used for collecting diagnostic data was inadequate for their needs.[68] The majority of these contractors wanted improvements in the timeliness, amount, dissemination, types, accuracy, and detail of data. The *Uniform Test Report (UTR)* template addresses these concerns.

---

[67] Aeronautic Division of Wright-Patterson AFB. *Generic Integrated Maintenance Diagnostics (GIMADS) Task 12*. Draft of February 19, 1990, p. D-438.

[68] Aeronautical Systems Division of Wright-Patterson AFB. *Generic Integrated Maintenance Diagnostics Task 12*. Draft, February 19, 1990, p. D-51.

Setting up a uniform test report format

A key function to be specified by contract is a reporting format that will drive the collection of life and reliability data during all testing, including DT&E and OT&E testing. The inclusion of reliability development (TAAF) tests and other life measuring tests in the project is essential to project risk reduction. Critical subcontractor equipment should be included and test results should be reported to project management.

The standard format should include specifications of graphical methods for presenting test data. Trend charts, possibly also showing confidence intervals, can show whether system reliability (e.g., Mean Time Between Failures [MTBF]) is improving.

Setting up a project-wide test-results database

Project management should set up a single, computerized database for recording test data and all test failures. High confidence in the design maturity of the system will be aided by an adequate data collection system to measure performance and current reliability levels. The contractor's Failure-Reporting and Corrective-Action System (FRACAS) is important, but a field data collection system designed for measurement of reliability as well as performance is also necessary. Consideration of this need during the planning stages will ensure that an adequate system is ready during evaluation tests. Continuous measurement of reliability growth will add to confidence in fielding a system with low risk. Any of the project's contractors should be able to query (but not modify) this database from their terminals or computers, to learn the status of any failure report entered previously. This database also should:

- Compute and plot statistics such as the Mean Time Between Failures (MTBF)

- Provide summaries and special reports for project management, designers, programmers, and manufacturing engineers

Examples of Uniform Test Report (UTR) formats

The upper half of Figure 17 provides an example of a UTR format that is useful for summarizing the results of formal reliability testing. This figure shows calculations of the *cumulative* and the *instantaneous* Mean Time Between Failure (MTBF) (mentioned in the TAAF chapter) at the stages of testing illustrated in the lower half of this figure. This alignment illustrates that integrated testing by subcontractors, the prime contractor, and the government can contribute data points to

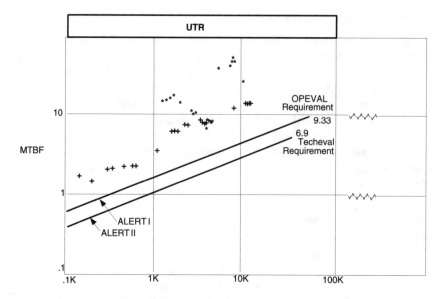

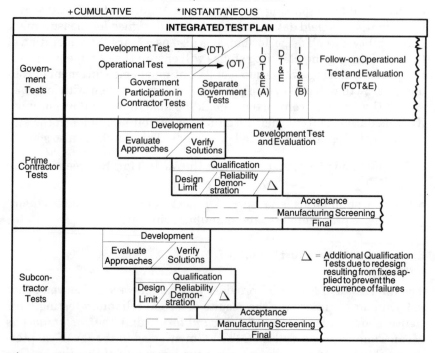

Figure 17 Relation between integrated test plan and UTR.

Figure 17 at all phases of the testing, including development, qualification, and acceptance testing.

The two parallel, sloping lines on Figure 17 show growth slope needed to achieve technical-evaluation and operational-evaluation requirements imposed by the Government. If the MTBF were to drop below these lines, the resulting "alerts" should trigger various management initiatives necessary to bring the program back on track. This may require special "Tiger Teams" to accelerate failure analysis and corrective actions or the shifting of additional resources to subsystems having design problems.

8

Field Feedback

Early report of problems that occur during initial system use helps eliminate design and manufacturing defects.

Feedback about field problems, however, often arrives late and incomplete, and analysts do not get failed parts soon enough. Military data-reporting systems often cannot provide complete and accurate reports of operating times, operating environments, and failure effects.

Contractor personnel can help the *Field Feedback* process. In some cases contractors participate in providing field feedback because they remain involved until the system is fully deployed.

Introduction

Field feedback is complete and accurate reporting of system failures, possible causes, and details about operating durations and operating environments. For this purpose, an efficient Failure-Reporting, Analysis, and Corrective-Action System (FRACAS) needs to be established before field operations start. This can be the same FRACAS used to support Integrated Test and TAAF during development, or the government and manufacturers can create a special FRACAS for field feedback.

The Field Feedback template specifies procedures for the control and handling of failed hardware, complaints concerning deficiencies, and warranty claims received from the customer. The following are important aspects of Field Feedback that should be included in contractors' agreements:

- *On-site feedback.* The contractor responsible for maintenance should send observers to the field to collect data on failures and field performance. Observers should not act as design engineers and should not try to implement hasty corrective actions in the field.

- *Failure reporting, analysis, and corrective actions.* After collecting field data, the contractor and government should report the data to design and manufacturing engineers for analysis and corrective actions. Those engineers should perform a root-cause analysis on all failures.

- *Timely return of failed parts to the contractor's analysis center.* Delay in returning failed parts for analysis results in replacing failed parts rather than eliminating the problem causing the failures. As a result, the system will continue to fail.

Field feedback can be obtained from many sources: installation reports, maintenance reports, customer trouble reports, repair reports, return reports, warranty reports, customer support groups, and end users. All of this data should be kept together in one database.

Field feedback can eliminate unforeseen design defects and correct problems caused during the transition from full-scale development to full-rate production. Developers must receive early notice of problems occurring during initial system use to eliminate design deficiencies as soon as possible. Efficient Field Feedback can improve the quality and timeliness of factory failure-mode analysis (FMA) and get field experience to research and development.

Risks and their consequences

Table 8 summarizes the risks and consequences addressed by Field Feedback.

TABLE 8   Risks and Consequences Addressed by Field Feedback

Risks	Consequences
Data and failed parts do not reach manufacturer	Manufacturer cannot correct failure causes
Failed parts delivered late	Correctable problems persist longer than necessary when analysts can't study them
Failure analysis omits operation-site analysis	Essential information from an on-site inspection cannot help improve design
Returned equipment lacks proper labeling	Analysts cannot identify and eliminate design and manufacturing problems
Standard military system collects data	Contractor data does not augment military data
	Technical assessment of field problems is incomplete

Risk: Data and failed parts do not reach manufacturer

For the manufacturer to understand the cause of and avoid future failures, test analysts must have access to failed parts for analysis and pertinent information.

Risk: Failed parts delivered late

If testers do not return failed parts in a timely manner, they delay early elimination of system problems. Delays in fixing system problems can cause repeated failures in the field and wasted spare parts.

Risk: Failure analysis omits operation-site analysis

Although failure analysis at the contractor's facility may reveal some causes of system deficiency, it may not assess a failure completely unless on-site analysis is available. On-site analysis preserves information about the failure at the time when failure occurred and helps explain the circumstances under which the failure occurred.

Risk: Returned equipment lacks proper labeling

It is practically impossible to analyze a failure if the engineers do not know what the problem is and what circumstances prevailed when the failure occurred. The cause of the failure may remain unknown because of inadequate labeling.

Risk: Standard military system collects data

Military data-collection systems may not be designed so that they encourage collection of data. Also, the databases may not be kept up to date. Contractor data collected during the transition to production, during production, and from the field will help determine the root cause of the failure.

A key to mission success is having an on-site engineering team and an on-site analysis process.

Procedures

Field Feedback reveals unforeseen design defects during field operation.

Benefits

Field Feedback:

- allows testers to evaluate a system under actual field performance
- makes available detailed and timely information about field problems. This information can improve products at a minimal cost
- helps assess system problems in the field accurately. This information helps developers design and produce the next system

Field Feedback provides information to the acquisition team to achieve:

- better system design
- higher product yield
- better product quality
- less repair and retest
- less scrap (during production)
- lower cost
- higher operational availability

Field Feedback covers such field functions as: installation, maintenance, trouble reports, warranty returns, and repairs.

Figure 18 shows a schematic of the Field Feedback process.

Field-failure types

Field failures differ for different systems.[69] Some types of failures in the field are:

- Cannot Duplicate (CND)—Cannot duplicate is an observed or recorded system malfunction that test engineers could not duplicate or verify at the factory or laboratory.
- Retest Okay (RTOK)—Retest okay refers to a unit that malfunctioned at one level, but whose specific malfunction cannot be duplicated at another operational level.
- Intermittent—Intermittent refers to a recurring fault that is present in a system for a limited period of time and then disappears.

---

[69]Aeronautic Division of Wright-Patterson AFB. *Generic Integrated Maintenance Diagnostics*. Draft of February 1990, p. 35.

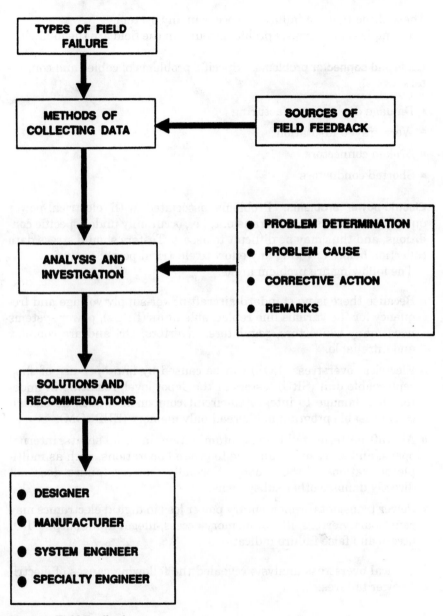

Figure 18 Field Feedback.

These three types of failure can occur in any system.

Examples of the type of problems found in the field are the following.

Cable and connector problems. Specific problems of cables and connectors are:

- Damage due to manufacturing
- Worn/frayed insulation
- Broken connectors
- Shorted conductors

Electric-power problems. Problems associated with electrical-power quality on systems can be transient, i.e., occur only under specific conditions, and thus may be difficult to assess. Testers should stress data collection before devoting any effort to electrical-power analysis.

The following are problem areas:[70]

- Because there is no standard aircraft power-supply voltage and frequency for the various line replaceable units (LRUs), power systems need many converters, regulators, inverters, etc. and are complex and unreliable.
- Electrical overstress (EOS) can be caused by improper use of shop replaceable unit (SRU) testers at the depot level, resulting in undetectable damage to integrated-circuit components, such as electrically erasable programmable read-only memory (EEPROM).
- Aircraft batteries fail from: contamination, internal shorts, internal opens, and excessive drain due to ground operations, such as multiple activations of the canopy. Normally, battery failure does not directly damage other subsystems.
- Power transients or momentary power loss in digital electronics may cause parity errors, illegal memory access, illegal input/output (I/O) access and false failure indications.

Electrical overstress analysis revealed the following causes of electrical-power failures:[71]

---

[70]Aeronautic Division of Wright-Patterson AFB. *Generic Integrated Maintenance Diagnostics*. Draft of February 19, 1990. pp. 1–124.

[71]Aeronautic Division of Wright-Patterson AFB. *Generic Integrated Maintenance Diagnostics*. Draft of February 19, 1990. pp. 1–124.

- Design: system interface, out of tolerance, overloading, underloading, wiring, connectors, surge protection, filtering techniques, breakers, transformers, grounding, and inadequate radiation tolerance
- Servicing: testers, maintenance facilities, test configurations, technical orders
- Power Generation: changing from one power source to another while the system is in use (e.g., switching from main power to emergency power), problems induced by mechanical failure, electromagnetic interference, electromagnetic pulse, electrostatic discharge
- Standardization: Using improper size and type of batteries and battery chargers

Mechanical systems. The data on a number of airplanes and M1-A1 tanks indicate the following mechanical failures:

- Airframe structures
- Landing gear
- Wheels and brakes
- Flight controls—mechanical and hydraulic
- Propulsions—engine and accessories
- Secondary power—auxiliary jet-fuel starter, gearboxes
- Hydraulic
- Pneumatic
- Steering
- Electrical
- Fuel
- Oxygen systems
- Environmental control systems
- Utility systems

The following failures are the most difficult to diagnose:

- Mechanical-system failures outside electrical control loops
- Transient failures that occur in-flight and cannot be reproduced on the ground
- Internal fluid leakage
- Compressor stalls
- Failure of gearboxes, transmissions, and engine-shaft bearings

- Unbonds or cracks in composite structures
- Intermittent problems due to temperature, and contamination of electrical contacts
- Sensor, cable, and connector failures
- Partially failed seals or partially blocked flow paths
- Undetected failures made evident from secondary effects
- Fuel-flow imbalance and quantity problems
- Small-engine power or performance failures

Electronic systems. The following may cause failures in electronic systems:

- Incomplete or faulty diagnostic capability
- Use of newly developed subsystems in previously developed systems without testing compatibility
- Not finding the root causes of previous failures: maintenance testing that uses built-in test (BIT), BIT plus test equipment, or manual rather than BIT or automatic testing that may not reveal the root cause of failures

Methods of collecting data

The best method of collecting data for Field Feedback uses a computerized database. All design engineers and design analysts should have access to these databases to analyze field failures.

A comprehensive method of collecting data provides a problem sheet to field operators and the contractor's observers. The problem sheet asks specific questions about system failures and related information. Table 9, Part A, shows the type of data the field operator and the field observer collect and record on the problem sheet.

Testers should forward the failed part and the problem sheet to the analysis center for evaluation. Part B of the problem sheet shows the type of activities performed by the analysis center. After completing the analysis and implementing the corrective action, the analysis center completes the second part of the problem sheet, Part B, and sends it to the database center for archiving.

Sources of Field Feedback. Possible sources of Field Feedback are:

- system users
- field operations
- on-site contractor engineering teams

TABLE 9   A Typical Problem Sheet

PART A. Field Feedback data collected by field personnel	
Category	General area of problem, e.g., cannot duplicate, cables, connectors, power, mechanical, software, electronics
System	Name of the faulty system(s), e.g., radar, radio, engine
Subsystem	Name of the faulty subsystem, e.g., power supply, compressor
Type of problem	No output, procedure, maintenance, intermittent
Data sources	Organization or database providing the information, e.g., aircraft base, naval weapon center, shipboard
Magnitude of problem	Scope of the problem, e.g., the number or frequency of occurrences
Problem description	Narrative description of the problem
Originator	Name of the person who provided the data documenting the fault
PART B. Field Feedback Data from the analysis and corrective action center	
Problem determination	Methods used to diagnose the problem
Problem cause	Narrative description of the cause
Corrective action	How analysts solved or will solve the problem
Design	Changes proposed in the design of the system
Diagnostic	Changes planned to improve system diagnostics
Remarks	Additional comments about the problem

- maintenance, depot, and contractor-operated service centers
- inventory accumulation points

Analysis and investigation

It is often harder to find the source of system failure than to design the system. Therefore those who analyze failures need troubleshooting experience and detailed knowledge of the system.

Often failure analysis and design are done by two separate groups. Some contractors prefer to rotate senior engineers between design and failure-analysis positions. Detailed knowledge of the system design can help them discover what failed, and failure-analysis work can lead to more-careful design of the next system.

Faults and fault analysis can take many forms, depending on the type of system and failure. Sometimes the cause of the fault is obvious, e.g., when a nail is found in a flat tire. Often the cause of the fault is subtle. For example, when the space-shuttle *Challenger* blew up, the cause could have been engine failure, fuel-plumbing leaks, or hundreds of other faults, singly or in combination. Fault analysts eventually blamed the "O rings" that sealed together cylindrical sections of the rocket motors.

Sometimes the system is so damaged that the only way to discover what failed first is for analysts to repeat the failure scenario with a fully instrumented system and record the sequence of cascading failures automatically.

Solutions and recommendations

After analyzing the problem, analysts list the probable causes of the problem for relevant organizations, e.g., design, manufacturing, and systems engineering.

The solution may include changes to system design, system operation, and system mission. Emerging diagnostic technologies and requirements that insist on their use may fix Cannot Duplicate's and ReTest OK's.

Typical failures handled by Field Feedback. Typical system problems reported through Field Feedback are:

- Manufacturing defects
- Intermittent problems, which are the most difficult problems for failure analysts
- Poor system design
- Improper system application
- Defective spares

Common problems in Field Feedback. Common problems with current feedback processes are:

- Delays in reporting field failures
- No on-site engineering inspections
- Poor labeling of failed parts
- Parts damaged during removal

Knowledge of these and other Field Feedback problems will help acquisition teams improve and prevent these problems from recurring.

Application

This chapter presents six applications of the methods and techniques suggested by the test templates Integrated Test; Failure Reporting System; Design Limit; Life; Test, Analyze, and Fix; Uniform Test Report; and Field Feedback.

These applications are:

- F/A-18 Hornet
- TEMP Format
- Life Expectancy of Wire
- Cathode Life Testing at RADC
- MK-15 Phalanx Close-In Weapon System
- SYSTEM 75 International DEFINITY PBX[72]

F/A-18 Hornet

In the early 1970s the Navy began developing its new, more-reliable Strike Fighter, the F/A-18 Hornet. Table 10 summarizes the objectives, milestones, and key contractors of the F/A-18 Hornet program.

Steps to reliability

Because the Navy's earlier strike fighter was often not ready to perform missions, reliability was a key objective of the F/A-18 Hornet. The Navy took several unusual steps to ensure reliability.

Reliability by contract. To ensure contractor commitment to reliability, the Navy wrote reliability guarantees into the F/A-18 contract. For

---

[72]SYSTEM 75 and DEFINITY are registered trademarks of AT&T.

TABLE 10   Objectives, Milestones, and Developers of the F/A-18 Hornet Program

Objectives	■ Multi-mission flexibility ■ Lower life-cycle cost ■ High reliability ■ Low maintenance ■ Improved readiness
Milestones	■ Contract awarded January 1976 ■ First flight in November 1978 ■ Canadian contract signed April 1980 ■ Defense System-Acquisition Review Council (DSARC) review in February 1981
Major contractors	■ McDonnell Aircraft Company, prime contractor for the airframe ■ Northrop Aircraft Company, major subcontractor for the airframe ■ General Electric Company, prime contractor for the F404 engine ■ Hughes Aircraft Company, subcontractor for radar

example, the contract guaranteed a mean flight hours between failure (MFHBF) of 3.7. The customer insisted that contractors accord these guarantees the same importance as other performance and cost goals.

Money incentives. The Navy offered contractors cash awards for achieving reliability goals. For example, contractors could receive $4 million for achieving the reliability guarantees after 1200 hours of flight tests, or $8 million for achieving the reliability guarantee during a 50-flight test of a single airplane.

Test, analyze, and fix (TAAF). The Navy asked for and paid for reliability development testing that exposed the F/A-18 subsystems and systems to mission-profile environments. For example, the usual test standard for temperature variation (MIL-STD-781) calls for slow temperature change from 160°F to minus 65°F over three hours; the realistic temperature-shock test of F/A-18 Hornet avionics cycled through that temperature range in 25 minutes.[73] Cockpit-mounted avionics, which sit inactive at high temperatures on hot sunny days with the canopy closed, begin tests at 203°F and quickly cool in response to ventilation.[74] Another mission profile reliability-development test that

---

[73]McDonnell Douglas Corporation. "Reliability Attainment." MDC IRAD, vol. 3. Project No. MDC Q0863-7. January 15, 1982, pp. 127450.06–127450.07.

[74]Rogger, W. R. *F/A-18 Hornet: Reliability Development Testing.* Philadelphia: 1985 Proceedings of the Annual Reliability and Maintainability Symposium, January 22–24, 1985, p. 4.

revealed many potential failures and improved reliability was a vibration test that used strong, *random* vibration rather than weak periodic sinusoidal vibration to simulate actual mission conditions.

Failure Reporting, Analysis and Corrective Action System (FRACAS). The Navy asked contractors to record, analyze, and correct F/A-18 failures by using a closed-loop evaluation and reporting system, i.e., FRACAS, to report and track all equipment failures.

Designed-in reliability. The Navy advocated reliability that is designed-in. Reliability engineers worked closely with designers and subsystem managers. They reviewed design details for reliability impact. They used over 400 trade studies to assess changes to the baseline design. Designing for reliability resulted in solid-state radar avionics having 8,000 fewer parts than an earlier fighter airplane and *derated* components, i.e., components operated comfortably below their nominal limits.

Figure 19 shows the estimated contribution of the above steps to the reliability of the F/A-18 Hornet.[75] As test hours accrue, reliability grows much faster than business-as-usual reliability.

---

[75]Ricketts, M. P. "F/A-18 Hornet Reliability Challenge: Status Report," Los Angeles: *1982 Proceedings of the Annual Reliability and Maintainability Symposium,* January 26–28, 1982, p. 4.

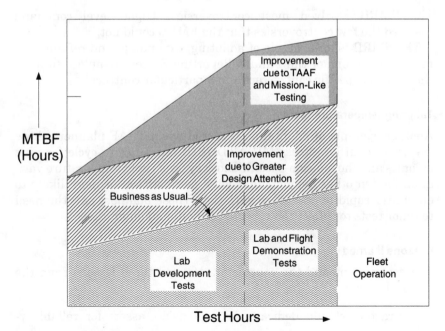

Figure 19 Strategies that improved F/A-18 reliability.

The result of the F/A-18 Hornet program is a reliable strike fighter. Contractors did not achieve the contract-guaranteed 3.7-MFHBF reliability after 1200 hours of flight tests and lost a $4 million incentive award. However, after about 2500 flight hours, they achieved a MFHBF of 8.4 during the grueling 50-flight test of a single aircraft, more than twice the 3.7-MFHBF guarantee. The contract allowed seven flight failures among the 50 flights, but the airplane failed only twice. McDonnell Aircraft Company won an $8 million incentive award.

Fitting the FRB to the F/A-18

Instead of a Failure Review Board, the F/A-18 Hornet program used a Reliability/Maintainability Review Board (RMRB) that the Navy and contractors jointly staffed and ran. In addition to monitoring failures, the RMRB studied unscheduled maintenance actions during flight-test operation and decided whether to include them in its reliability database, i.e., the FRACAS and UTR.

The RMRB excluded from the reliability database unscheduled maintenance that:

- resulted from test-equipment problems
- was non-relevant per Navy maintenance guidelines, or
- could not recur given previously approved design changes

The RMRB resolved most controversies. Higher-level command resolved the few controversies that the RMRB could not.

The RMRB is an example of adapting, expanding, and refining the recommendations of the Failure Reporting System template to meet the needs of specific contractors and a particular contract.

Tailoring temperature tests

Another example of adaptation occurred when TAAF planners chose the traditional low-stress MIL-STD-781B temperature cycle for nine avionics and the mission-specific shock cycle of rapid temperature variation for ten other avionics that were more critical or more likely to encounter rapid temperature variation. Those planners saw the need to tailor tests to reflect the expected operational environment.

Lessons learned

The government and the contractors learned these lessons from the F/A-18 Hornet:

- Contractors should dedicate, i.e., set aside, assets for reliability-growth testing.[76] Otherwise reliability testing competes with development testing for scarce resources, and one or the other suffers.

- Contractors and the government should emphasize the test-and-fix process of TAAF over tracking MTBF because this encourages the most testing, the most failures, and the most fixes. Without this emphasis, the goals of the government and contractors conflict: the government wants lots of tests and believes a successful test results in many failures and fixes; contractors are reluctant to test because more tests mean more chances for system failure, and failures lower MTBF calculations, which contractors need to raise. Emphasizing test-and-fix TAAF over MTBF calculations can allay contractor fears that doing tests may hurt them and can help contractors share the government's enthusiasm for maximizing failures.[77]

- Tests should reflect real mission conditions, which the government and the contractors must define early. The F/A-18 program did this by carefully analyzing training flights, missions, and ground operations. Flight conditions used in tests included combat maneuvers and occasional design-limit conditions. Ground operations included the effects of transport, flight preparation, maintenance, and storage. By using realistic test requirements that kept system test conditions within system design limits, testers avoided having to treat failures that will never occur in the field.[78]

- The contract should require measurement of the speed, cost-effectiveness, success, and other aspects of corrective actions. Measurement of system reliability does not reveal enough about development progress.[79]

- Planners should limit reliability-development testing to high-risk or critical systems because TAAF consumes people and materiel. Not

[76]Rogger, W. R. *F/A-18 Hornet: Reliability Development Testing.* Philadelphia: 1985 Proceedings of the Annual Reliability and Maintainability Symposium, January 22–24, 1985, p. 6.

[77]Rogger, W. R. *F/A-18 Hornet: Reliability Development Testing.* Philadelphia: 1985 Proceedings of the Annual Reliability and Maintainability Symposium, January 22–24, 1985, p. 4.

[78]Rogger, W. R. *F/A-18 Hornet: Reliability Development Testing.* Philadelphia: 1985 Proceedings of the Annual Reliability and Maintainability Symposium, January 22–24, 1985, p. 2.

[79]Rogger, W. R. *F/A-18 Hornet: Reliability Development Testing.* Philadelphia: 1985 Proceedings of the Annual Reliability and Maintainability Symposium, January 22–24, 1985, p. 1.

unexpectedly, the F/A-18 program erred in predicting which subsystems needed testing and which were already reliable.[80]

- Participants in a major development must expect surprises. The F/A-18 program used new, sophisticated test chambers, test rigs, and test procedures that caused delays. Redesigns, e.g., of castings, were slow. TAAF competed with aircraft needs and other programs for supplier resources.[81]

TEMP Format

The Test-and-Evaluation Master Plan (TEMP) is the government's outline of Development Test and Evaluation (DT&E) and Operational Test and Evaluation (OT&E).

Table 11 shows the TEMP's five-part format from DoD 5000.3-M-1, which readers needing TEMP details should consult.[82] A standard format helps diverse organizations select information for their planning.

Life Expectancy of Telephone-Wire Insulation[83]

Polyethylene, a plastic used as an insulation over the copper conductor in telephone wire, can oxidize in the presence of atmospheric oxygen (and ozone), especially in a hot geographical location, e.g., San Luis and Yuma in Arizona. Environmental conditions, such as air pollution, and residential-cable filling compound remaining on the wire insulation can accelerate oxidation and lead to a shorter life for the wire insulation.

As a result of the oxidation of insulation, copper wire loses its ability to carry data and voice, resulting in deteriorated telephone service. The rate of oxidation is higher in high-temperature and highly polluted environments. Yuma's average annual temperature is 30°C. This figure can go as high as 50°C in the summer. The town's air is highly pol-

---

[80]Rogger, W. R. *F/A-18 Hornet: Reliability Development Testing.* Philadelphia: 1985 Proceedings of the Annual Reliability and Maintainability Symposium, January 22–24, 1985, p. 2.

[81]Rogger, W. R. *F/A-18 Hornet: Reliability Development Testing.* Philadelphia: 1985 Proceedings of the Annual Reliability and Maintainability Symposium, January 22–24, 1985, p. 5

[82]Department of Defense. *5000.3-M-1. Test and Evaluation Master Plan Guidelines.*

[83]Khorramian, B. A. and Washington, Y. M., "The Environmental Effects on the Thermal Oxidation of DEPIC Wire Insulations." AT&T Bell Laboratories. Atlanta, GA, June 26, 1987.

**TABLE 11   Outline of the Test-and-Evaluation
Master Plan**
Test-and-Evaluation Master Plan

Part I. System Description
1. Mission Description
2. System Description
3. Required Technical Characteristics
4. Required Operational Characteristics

Part II. Program Summary
1. Management
2. Integrated Schedule

Part III. DT&E Outline
1. Critical Technical Characteristics
2. DT&E's to Date
3. Special Requirements for System or Subsystem Retest
4. Future DT&E

PART IV. OT&E Outline
1. Critical Operational Issues
2. OT&E to Date
3. Future OT&E

PART V. Resource Summary
1. Systems to be Tested and Test Support Equipment
2. Test Sites and Instrumentation
3. Test-Support Equipment
4. Threat Systems
5. Test Goals
6. Operational-Force Test Support
7. Simulators, Models, and Test-beds
8. Special Requirements
9. T&E Funding Requirements
10. Resource Schedule
11. People and Training

luted with suspended particulates. The total suspended particulates (TSPs) in Yuma's air result from:

- Insecticides and pesticides used in local agriculture stay suspended in the atmosphere.
- Airplane activity—Four airplane operations pollute the air in Yuma: a) Marine Corps Air Station, b) McDonnell Douglas Test Facility,

c) Yuma Proving Grounds (Army), and d) Civilian Air Traffic. Supersonic airplane activity takes place 24 hours a day in the Yuma area.

■ Upper-atmosphere ozone-layer thinning—The resulting direct ultraviolet (UV) radiation from the sun produces ozone from molecular oxygen on the surface of the earth, and ozone has an adverse effect on exposed wire insulation.

Experiment

AT&T Bell Laboratories studied a Yuma telephone cable containing insulated wire. AT&T manufactured the cable in Atlanta in 1978, and designated it ALTW 100. The filling compound was petroleum jelly. The standard, production cable began service in September 1978 in Yuma. Ten feet of the insulated wires, including a portion exposed to the atmosphere, were removed in June 1986 and used in this study. Normally, part of the exposed portion of the cable core inside the pedestal is bent, as illustrated in Figure 20.

None of the insulation studied showed any sign of cracking. Experimenters divided the unsheathed cable into three sections: Section I was close to the cable sheath, Section II was the bent area, and Section III was the free end of the exposed wire. They also tested samples of the insulated wire that had remained sheathed.

Particulates covered all three sections of the insulated wires used in this study, presumably from particles suspended in the air. These particulates appeared as dirt attached to the cable-filling compound covering the insulation. Wire insulation with particulates attached is designated "as is" in this study. After removing the particulates with a paper towel, the wire is designated "cleaned."

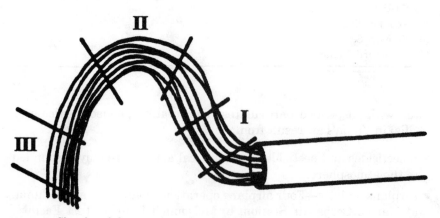

Figure 20 Sheath and three sections of unsheathed wire.

This study uses the undersheath wire insulation to compare its oxidation induction time (OIT) values to those of exposed wires, thus showing the effect of the environment on the stability of wire insulation. In this regard, the "as is" and "cleaned" samples for OIT measurements were adjacent to each other to eliminate location differences.

OIT measurements (accelerating the time of oxidation). For the purposes of this study, the oxidation induction time (OIT) is the time it takes the insulation to undergo auto-catalytic oxidation when exposed continuously to a pure-oxygen, high-temperature environment. Auto-catalytic oxidation, which is less dramatic than burning, appears as a sudden release of heat that quickly chars the insulation. It probably involves a chain-reaction of oxidizing molecules. High oxygen concentration (100% oxygen) and high temperatures (from 130°C to 200°C) accelerate normal oxidation. Actual oxygen concentration in air is 21% and the temperature in Yuma is less than 50°C.

The OIT temperatures ranged from 130 to 200°C at 10°C intervals, with exceptions as noted in Tables 12 and 13. All OIT data were obtained from a single test unless the result was in doubt, in which case the test was repeated.

Experimenters used a modified Arrhenius equation to evaluate the effect of environmental conditions and filling compound on the life of wire insulation.

The average field temperature of Yuma is taken to be 40°C. The OIT values were extrapolated to this temperature for three sections of "as is" and "cleaned" samples of the exposed insulation. Data indicated that due to the mixture of particulate and filling compound on wire insulation, the estimated OIT at 40°C dropped from 126, 137, and 100 years to 18.7, 19.1, and 10.4 years for Sections I, II, and III, respectively.

TABLE 12   OIT (in min.) of Yuma 1978 Cable-Wire Insulation at Various Temperatures

Oxidation Temp.°C	Section I		Section II		Section III		Under Sheath*	
	As Is	Cleaned	As Is	Cleaned	As Is	Cleaned	As Is	Cleaned**
130	302	452	57	160	64	131	—	—
140	41	75	28	71	31	74	—	—
150	12	30	11	25	13	33	880	970
160	5.2	11	3.0	9.2	4.3	14	370	430
170	3.1	5.2	2.0	4.3	2.1	4.2	130	160
180	1.9	3.1	0.6	1.3	0.8	1.6	61	69
190	1.1	1.1	0.3	0.5	0.5	0.5	18	16
200	0.5	0.5	0	0.2	0	0.2	5.9	5.1

*"Under Sheath" means sheathed insulated wire from buried, compound-filled telephone cable not exposed to atmospheric conditions.
**"Cleaned" refers to the sample where filling compound was wiped off.

TABLE 13   OIT (in min.) of Yuma 1978 Cable-Wire Insulation at Various Temperatures

Oxidation Temp.°C	Insulation Color	Section I		Section II		Section III	
		As Is	Cleaned	As Is	Cleaned	As Is	Cleaned
140	Black	62	43	71	70	50	45
150	Black	59	27	63	59	41	27
160	Black	20	19	32	22	18	16
170	Black	11	10	13	10	5.4	4.7
140	White	44	32	39	37	45	37
150	White	21	19	19	19	21	18
160	White	11	6.6	7.4	7.0	8.0	6.0
170	White	3.3	3.6	2.8	3.3	3.8	3.8

Lessons learned

At the time of this study, the field life of exposed wire insulation was in the range of 8 to 10 years. The values obtained from accelerated testing ranged from 10.4 to 18.7 years. The discrepancy can be a warning that even with careful testing, the life expectancy from accelerated tests and the real life expectancy can be quite different.

The estimated values here are based on extrapolation of OIT data obtained above the melting point of polyethylene insulation, i.e., 125°C. Because of crystallinity differences above and below the melting point, the data obtained above the melting point cannot be extrapolated reliably to temperatures below the melting point. Thus, life data and the acceleration factor obtained at a higher temperature may not be valid at a lower temperature.

Cathode Life Testing at RADC

The Rome Air Development Center (RADC) has responded to the tri-service and NASA need for ultra-long-life cathodes by establishing the RADC Cathode Life Test Facility.[84] Cathode life is critical in satellites and other space applications where maintenance is difficult. The cathodes studied are thermionic cathodes in traveling-wave tubes, that is, the cathode is a hot, metallic element that emits electrons.

Many new types of cathode offer promise, but they lack performance credentials for long life because of insufficient testing. Long life for a cathode is life that exceeds 100,000 hours. From 1980 to 1990, RADC

---

[84]Bussey, D., Daniszewski, E., Novak, M., Ryan, J., and Wilkinson, J. "RADC Cathode Life Test Program." *IEEE Transactions on Electron Devices*, vol. 37(12), December 1990, pp. 2612–2613.

logged more than 1.5 million hours of tests on a variety of cathodes. Cathode types include B, M, Mixed-Metal Matrix, Trilayer, Transition Metal, Reservoir, Siemens MK, Co-Deposited, and Controlled-Porosity Dispenser.

RADC tests cathodes by mounting them on vehicles that simulate actual operating conditions and by operating them in continuous-wave mode, which is more harsh than pulsed-mode operation. Continuous-wave testing gives a conservative, minimum estimate of cathode life.

Initial-cathode-activity plots serve as the baseline for comparison and vehicle-performance analysis. Figure 21 is an initial-activity plot for several cathode types that shows the temperature dependence of cathode output current as a percent of rated output current. The "knee" of these plots, i.e., the temperature at which the output current levels off, also determines the operating temperature to use during life tests. RADC finds that 50°C above the knee is the best operating temperature for each cathode.

RADC uses a two-color pyrometer to obtain consistent measurements of cathode temperature on the test vehicles. Using a special pyrometer technique, RADC achieved these advantages over earlier temperature measurements:

- Measurements are more repeatable.
- The setup time is shorter.

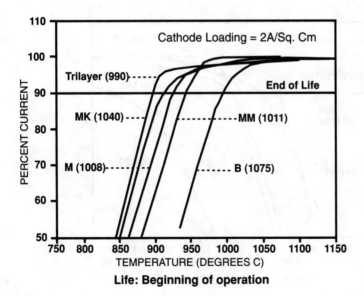

Figure 21 Initial activity plot for long-life cathodes.

- Adjustments cancel the effects of any jarring during instrument setup.
- Different testers obtain similar results.

The RADC Cathode Life Test Facility uses no accelerated tests. However, RADC is studying accelerated testing as a way to get more testing out of the forty power supplies now available in the facility. Namely, by screening new cathodes to select the most promising candidates, power-supply resources exercise those cathodes most likely to meet government needs.

Figure 22 compares the activity (output current) of various cathode types after about 20,000 hours of operation, again as a function of true temperature. The mixed-metal matrix is the cathode type that best sustains current output. It is being qualified for use in space.

The RADC Cathode Life Test Facility expects that technical advances in cathode design will quickly migrate to generally available devices. Meanwhile, it pursues its goal of supplying data about the "best" cathodes to manufacturers.

Phalanx Close-In Weapon System (CIWS)

The Phalanx Close-In Weapon System (CIWS) is a self-contained 20-millimeter quick-acting anti-missile gun with built-in systems for

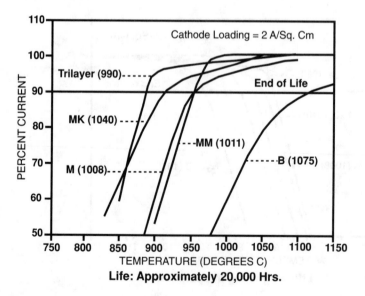

Figure 22 Cathode activity plot after 20,000 hours.

tracking targets and assessing target destruction. Intended for use on a ship to protect against airborne-missile attacks, the CIWS consists of search radar, a system that controls firing, a command-and-decision computer, and the gun.

According to a 1988 Transition Assessment Program survey team, the Test, Analyze, and Fix (TAAF) effort on the Phalanx brought close cooperation and coordination between the Navy and the contractor, General Dynamics. Spanning early 1987 through mid-1990, it impressed the Assistant Secretary of the Navy (Shipbuilding and Logistics).[85] [86]

Lessons learned

An important lesson learned from the Phalanx effort is the difficulty of doing disciplined TAAF under real-world constraints of cost and time. Early planning and up-front funding are key to successful TAAF.[87] Contractors who worked on other government projects echo these needs and say that, when the contract specifies the cost of TAAF, the procuring agency often cuts TAAF from the contract to save up-front costs. Even the Phalanx TAAF, despite careful planning, endured funding and scheduling constraints that limited testing. There were too few systems and spares available for testing.

Also key was the *and fix* part of TAAF and the development of an effective Phalanx corrective-action system (FRACAS) that ensured disciplined documentation and records. The FRACAS record-keeping system used standard notations that helped reconstruct and analyze earlier events.[88]

TAAF problems arose because no one knew how to put TAAF in the contractual terms and because neither the government nor the contractor had experience in conducting TAAF.

---

[85] Office of the Assistant Secretary of the Navy (Shipbuilding and Logistics). *Report of Survey of MK-15 Phalanx CIWS Program.* OASN (S&L), Reliability, Maintainability, and Quality-Assurance Directorate, September 14–16, 1988, p. 11.

[86] Higa, L. S. *Phalanx Close-In Weapon System Test Analyze and Fix (TAAF) Plan for Phalanx Block IR, TM 6-336-87-P-077D.* Pomona, CA: General Dynamics, September 13, 1988, p. 31.

[87] *Report of Survey of MK-15 Phalanx CIWS Program.* Office of the Assistant Secretary of the Navy (Shipbuilding and Logistics) Reliability, Maintainability, and Quality-Assurance Directorate, 14–16 September, 1988, p. 11.

[88] *Report of Survey of MK-15 Phalanx CIWS Program.* Office of the Assistant Secretary of the Navy (Shipbuilding and Logistics) Reliability, Maintainability, and Quality-Assurance Directorate, 14–16 September, 1988, p. 11.

To remedy this, the Navy and the contractor recommended improving the existing guidelines and directives on TAAF. As a result, a set of TAAF guidelines appeared early in 1989.[89] It includes a bibliography on TAAF and clarifies procedures for exposing equipment to stress and defining the duration of tests.

The Phalanx program review concluded that a properly done TAAF significantly reduces risk, but TAAF done poorly adds little value and drains resources.[90]

SYSTEM 75 International DEFINITY PBX[91]

Recently the AT&T System 75 International DEFINITY PBX development team wrote 70,000 lines of software code that were integrated with 900,000 pre-existing lines of code. This project also added new hardware (circuit boards) to pre-existing equipment. In previous projects, system testing had occurred only near the end of development, after design and coding had ended (see Figure 23). Unfortunately, this scheduling made it difficult and costly to use test results to improve the system, and system testing was prolonged.

This development project scheduled development and testing in stages in which small amounts of new software and hardware were joined to previously tested hardware and software. New tests, consisting of a random sample of the tests run at the end of development, were

DEVELOPMENT PROCESS

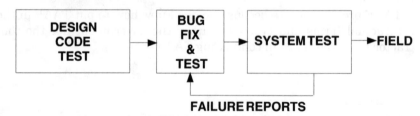

FAILURE REPORTS

Figure 23 Testing follows design and coding.

---

[89]*The TAAF Process, a Technical Brief for TAAF Implementation,* a joint publication of the U.S. Air Force (HQ USAF, LE-RD), Army (HQ AMC, QA), and Navy (OASN, S&L), Washington, DC: January 1989.

[90]*Report of Survey of MK-15 Phalanx CIWS Program.* Office of the Assistant Secretary of the Navy (Shipbuilding and Logistics) Reliability, Maintainability, and Quality-Assurance Directorate, 14–16 September, 1988, p. 11.

[91]SYSTEM 75 and DEFINITY are trademarks of AT&T.

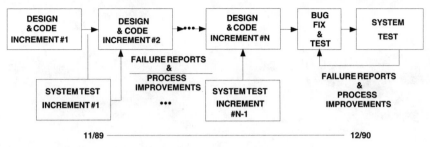

Figure 24 Testing is intermingled with design and coding.

run at the end of each stage of development. This strategy, which is illustrated in Figure 24, resulted in testing and redesigning throughout development. By making failures occur earlier, this strategy made it easier to correct problems as soon as they were detected. This strategy is a type of the integrated reliability-growth testing described in the *Test, Analyze, and Fix (TAAF)* template.

While previous projects had defined success as the percentage of modules of code passing tests, this project defined success as the percentage of simulated user scenarios working perfectly. No failures were ignored, even if they shared the same cause. This definition encouraged designers to prioritize their corrective actions to reflect customer needs. It also increased the accuracy with which testing results were used to predict end-users' success in using the deployed system. Also, not ignoring test failures resulting from a problem uncovered in a previous stage encouraged developers to eliminate failure causes before testing the next stage.

Although the project planners had to exert additional effort to plan staged development and testing, their efforts reduced the projected duration of the system-test interval by 25% (from four months to three months spread over the 20-month duration of the project) and achieved a lower ratio of testing time to total project time than several other similar projects had experienced. Another benefit of this strategy was lower field maintenance costs. On previous projects, development personnel were tied up with problem-fixing and could not start another project, but this project's quality was so high that staff allocated for fixing field-reported problems were not needed and could move on to other projects.

Summary

As explained in the Introduction and Procedures chapters, key methods of managing pre-mission testing are:

- *Planning* testing carefully
- *Coordinating* test schedules thoroughly
- *Identifying* the causes of test failures as quickly and thoroughly as possible
- *Correcting* all identified failure causes
- *Sharing* test facilities and test results cooperatively
- *Communicating* test requirements and results widely, using a common format and database (Uniform Test Report template)
- *Integrating* system planning and test planning to ensure that testing meets system needs
- *Organizing* for the planning and follow-through of testing by formalizing the test-planning and failure-analysis functions, e.g., by appointing a Test Planning Team (TPT) and a Failure Review Board (FRB).
- *Empowering* the FRB to order modifications to the system to correct the causes of test failures
- *Tracking* reliability measures such as MTBF during development to determine whether reliability is growing (i.e., improving)
- *Integrating* reliability-growth testing with development testing as much as possible
- *Combining* Operational Test and Evaluation (OT&E) with Development Test and Evaluation (DT&E), but not so thoroughly that OT&E cannot ensure that the system meets the government's needs
- *Making* process improvements routinely throughout development and production to improve manufacturability, maintainability, and reliability

- *Continuing* reliability-growth activities beyond the end of development, to analyze and remove the causes of failures found subsequently

Tables 14 through 20, respectively, outline the templates covered in this part:

- Integrated Test
- Failure Reporting System
- Design Limit
- Life
- Test, Analyze, and Fix
- Uniform Test Report
- Field Feedback

TABLE 14   Summary of the Integrated-Test Template

Facets of Integrated Test	Details
How to do Integrated Test	■ Project management forms a Test-Planning Team (TPT) ■ The TPT sets up the Uniform Test Report and test results database ■ The TPT plans what tests to do ■ Testers design the tests ■ Testers run tests and analysts study the results ■ Designers improve the system ■ The government does acceptance testing
People who make Integrated Test happen	■ Project management supports and implements ■ Test-planning team (TPT) plans tests ■ Operational Test Agency (OTA) does mission profile tests ■ Authors of test documents write ■ Test Designers design tests ■ Testers test and report results ■ Test analyzers study test results
Integrated Test documents	■ TEMP (Test-and-Evaluation Master Plan) is the government's outline of development and operational tests ■ ITP (Integrated Test Plan) is the contractors' outline of development tests ■ Each individual test plan gives details of one test

TABLE 15   Summary of the Failure-Reporting-System Template

Procedures	Supporting Activities
Designate a Control Organization	■ The Program Manager or an empowered manager chairs the control organization ■ The organization meets regularly (e.g., weekly or bi-weekly) or as needed ■ The organization exists for the duration of the project, including deployment
Perform Failure Reporting System activities	■ Using a single format, as in the Uniform Test Report (UTR), testers report each test failure ■ If possible, testers verify each failure by repeating it or obtaining physical evidence ■ Analysts study each failure to determine its cause ■ Designers change the system and project managers adjust operating procedures and maintenance to eliminate identified causes of failure ■ Testers verify that the changes remove the cause of failure ■ Trouble-report trackers close out the failure reports after successful corrective action ■ The control organization ensures that all failure reports remain open only a short time ■ Retention of failed hardware (e.g., piece parts) to compare with similar failures

TABLE 16   Summary of Design-Limit Testing Procedures

Procedures	Supporting Activities
Gather information	■ Provide design documentation to test engineers ■ Determine the life-cycle mission profile ■ Plan to integrate all possible tests ■ Plan to perform the environmental-design test and the operational environmental-verification test
Plan Design-Limit tests	■ Determine the "worst case" environment ■ Allocate the worst-case mission profile to appropriate subsystems ■ Decide which Design Limit test to perform ■ Integrate Design Limit tests with other tests
Obtain test resources	■ Get parts and reserve environmental chambers for appropriate tests
Perform tests	■ Document all results
Evaluate results	■ Use root-cause analysis to discover the reasons for mission-threatening failures

TABLE 17   Summary of Life Testing Procedures

Procedures	Supporting Activities
Conduct Life analyses of components, subsystems, and the system	■ Review historical data to analyze the life of the system ■ Use theoretical and graphical methods to analyze the life data
Plan aging tests	■ Choose well-known models that relate the life of the system to stresses ■ Plan and budget appropriately to prevent schedule slippage and delay in design improvement
Get parts for Life tests	■ Obtain the parts as soon as possible to start Life tests quickly
Perform tests and/or use models	■ Use known methods and models to determine the life of the system ■ Accelerated method ■ Arrhenius model ■ Eyring model ■ AT&T Reliability model ■ Power model
Evaluate results	■ Report the results of Life testing to design engineers for design improvements

TABLE 18   Summary of Test, Analyze, and Fix

Procedures	Supporting Activities
Prepare for reliability-growth testing	■ Reliability experts predict the reliabilities of subsystems and systems ■ Designers derate parts and materials to ensure and improve reliability ■ Test-results analysts perform Failure-Modes-and-Effects Analysis (FMEA) to find root causes ■ Reliability experts may recommend environmental-stress screening to disclose potential defects ■ Reliability experts choose a reliability-growth model, such as Duane or Crow (AMSAA), to compare expected and actual reliability growth ■ Reliability experts choose a reliability-growth rate for use with the reliability model ■ Testers predict the duration of reliability-growth testing
Perform tests and analyze the results	■ Analysts identify which failures are relevant and chargeable ■ Testers record test results, including successes ■ Reliability experts determine reliability growth ■ Analysts review the failures ■ Continuous improvement of manufacturing processes and system design is another way to improve reliability
Continue reliability growth beyond the end of pre-mission testing	■ The failure control organization continues to track and resolve failure modes appearing during manufacture, deployment, and use

TABLE 19   Summary of the Uniform-Test-Report Template

Procedures	Supporting Activities
Set up a Uniform Test Report (UTR) format	■ Project Management does this through the TPT and failure control organization ■ The UTR format should encourage graphical summarization and presentation of results, e.g., trend charts
Set up a project-wide test-results database	■ Project management, through the TPT and failure control organization, sets up and controls data entry into this database, which all contractors in the project will access

TABLE 20   Summary of Field Feedback and Its Procedures

Procedures	Supporting Activities
Avoid problems	Common problems in Field Feedback: ■ Delays in reporting field failures ■ No on-site engineering inspections ■ Lack of return of failed parts for analysis
Categorize field failures	Types of field failure include: ■ CND—Test engineers cannot duplicate a particular field failure in the laboratory ■ RTOK—Retest of a failed field system does not confirm the failure ■ Intermittent—Failures that randomly appear and disappear, causes unknown ■ Cable and connector problems ■ Electric-power problems ■ Mechanical problems ■ Electronic problems
Collect data	Possible sources of Field Feedback data are: ■ Field operators ■ On-site contractor engineering team ■ Maintenance centers ■ Depot centers ■ Company-operated service centers ■ Inventory accumulation points
Analyze and investigate	■ Describe the problem ■ Specify the magnitude of the problem ■ Focus on specifics of the problem ■ Identify the cause of the problem ■ Specify the corrective action
Recommend a solution	■ Give solution alternatives to design and manufacturing teams

11

References

AT&T Bell Laboratories. *Enhanced Modular Signal Processor Master Test Plan.* PMS 412, April 21, 1986. Describes topics in test support (quality assurance, configuration management, technical and logistics support); test flow (prototype, development, integration, verification milestones, documentation); organization and test management; milestones and schedules; test description; test objectives; test methods; and test-planning factors.

AT&T Bell Laboratories. *Reliability by Design.* Indianapolis, IN: AT&T Customer Information Center, 1989. Provides many methods for use during design to achieve improved reliability.

Benton, Alan W. and Crow, L. H. "Integrated Reliability Growth Testing." *IEEE Proceedings on Annual Reliability and Maintainability Symposium,* 1989, pp. 160–166. Describes reliability growth (reliability development) through testing and presents results and lessons learned from Army programs.

Best Manufacturing Practices. *Report of Survey Conducted at Bell Helicopter Textron.* Fort Worth, TX: October 1988. Describes Bell Helicopter Textron policy, practices, and strategy in the functional areas of design, test, production, facilities, logistics, management, and transition planning. Catalogs practices and relates them to critical-path templates of DoD 4245.7-M, *Transition from Development to Production.*

Best Manufacturing Practices. *Report of Survey Conducted at Litton Guidance and Guidance Systems Division.* Woodland Hills, CA: October 1985. Describes Litton Guidance and Guidance Systems Division policy, practices, and strategy in the functional areas of design, test, production, facilities, logistics, management, and transition planning. Catalogs practices and relates them to critical-path templates of DoD 4245.7-M, *Transition from Development to Production.*

Best Manufacturing Practices. *Report of Survey Conducted at Litton Systems Amecom Division.* College Park, MD: June 1989. Describes Litton Systems Amecom Division policy, practices, and strategy in the functional areas of design, test, production, facilities, logistics, management, and transition planning. Catalogs practices and relates them to critical-path templates of DoD 4245.7-M, *Transition from Development to Production.*

Best Manufacturing Practices. *Report of Survey Conducted at Teledyne Electronics.* Newbury Park, CA: July 1989. Describes Teledyne Electronics policy, practices, and strategy in the functional areas of design, test, production, facilities, logistics, management, and transition planning. Catalogs practices and relates them to critical-path templates of DoD 4245.7-M, *Transition from Development to Production.*

Best Manufacturing Practices. *Report of Survey Conducted at Northrop Aircraft Division.* Hawthorne, CA: March 1989. Describes Northrop Aircraft Division policy, practices, and strategy in the functional areas of design, test, production, facilities, logistics, management, and transition planning. Catalogs practices and relates them to critical-path templates of DoD 4245.7-M, *Transition from Development to Production.*

Crow, L. H. "Estimation Procedures for the Duane Model." Aberdeen Proving Ground, MD: *Proceedings US AMSAA Reliability Growth Symposium,* September 1972. Assumes the same growth pattern as the Duane procedure but formulates the occurrence of failures as a statistical (i.e., nonhomogeneous Poisson) process.

Crow, L. H. "New International Standards on Reliability Growth." *1991 Proceedings Annual Reliability and Maintainability Symposium.* Provides statistical procedures for projecting reliability after delayed fixes to the system.

Crow, L. H. "On the Initial System Reliability." *1986 Proceedings Annual Reliability and Maintainability Symposium.* Shows how to estimate initial system reliability at the start of development.

Crow, L. H. "Reliability Analysis for Complex Repairable Systems." Philadelphia, PA: *Reliability and Biometry,* Proshan, F. and Serfling, R. J., Eds., SIAM, 1974. Shows how to obtain confidence intervals for the Duane model of reliability.

Crow, L. H. "Reliability Growth Projection From Delayed Fixes." *1983 Proceedings, Annual Reliability and Maintainability Symposium,* 1983. Provides statistical procedures for estimating current reliability after delayed fixes to the system.

Crow, L. H. and Robbins, N. B. *The AT&T-FSAT Handbook on Integrated Reliability-Growth Testing.* To be published. Provides an in-depth description of integrated reliability-growth testing and its management.

Davis, B. *The Economics of Automatic Testing.* New York: McGraw-Hill, 1982. Describes the following areas of testing: economics of component and circuit-board testing, optimizing the testing strategy, fault coverage, automating field-service, evaluating automatic test equipment, calculation of equipment costs and yields, and financial appraisal in testing.

Departments of the Air Force, Army, and Navy. *The TAAF Process, a Technical Brief for TAAF Implementation.* Washington, DC: HQ USAF, LE-RD; HQ AMC, QA; and OASN, S&L; January 1989. Provides successful TAAF methods, which include management methods, engineering practices, and suggested contract language for program managers and engineers. Stresses the *and fix* aspect of TAAF: "In TAAF, failures are welcome." Clarifies procedures for exposing equipment to stress and defining the duration of tests. Includes a bibliography on TAAF.

Department of Defense. *MIL-HDBK-189, Military Handbook, Reliability Growth Management.* Washington, DC: DoD, February 13, 1981. Defines delayed fixes, which affect the estimates of failure rates (or MTBF) observed during reliability-growth testing.

Department of Defense. *MIL-STD-781D, Reliability Testing for Engineering Development, Qualification, and Production.* Washington, DC: DoD, October 17, 1987. Details reliability-growth programs, with emphasis on technical details of reliability tracking. Includes methods for contracting for reliability growth.

Department of Defense. *MIL-STD-785B, Reliability Program for Systems and Equipment Development and Production.* Washington, DC: DoD, September 15, 1980. Serves as a starting point for reliability-growth efforts in military project.

Department of Defense. *MIL-STD-1635 (EC), Reliability Growth Testing.* Washington, DC: DoD, February 3, 1978. Describes the Duane procedure for interpreting the results from reliability-growth testing.

Department of Defense. *MIL-STD-2155 (AS), Military Standard, Failure Reporting, Analysis and Corrective Action System.* Washington, DC: DoD, July 24, 1985. Describes the Failure Reporting, Analysis and Corrective Action System (FRACAS) for tracking, analyzing, and eliminating failures.

Department of Defense. *Transition from Development to Production.* DoD 4245.7-M, September 1985. Describes techniques for avoiding technical risks in 48 key areas or templates that include design, test, production, facilities, logistics, and management. Identifies critical engineering processes and controls for design, test, and production of low-risk products.

Department of Defense. *5000.3-M-1, Test and Evaluation Master Plan Guidelines.* Describes various aspects of test and evaluation: technical and operational characteristics of systems; management; scheduling; technical and operational characteristics of development test and evaluation; test-and-evaluation resources; and test-and-evaluation critical parameters.

Department of the Navy. *Best Practices: How to Avoid Surprises in the World's Most Complicated Technical Process.* NAVSO P-6071, March 1986. Describes how to avoid traps and risks by implementing best practices for 47 areas or templates that include design, test, production, facilities, logistics, and management. Provides program managers and contractors with an overview of the key issues and best practices to improve the acquisition life cycle.

Defense Systems Management College. *Test and Evaluation Management Guide.* Fort Belvoir, VA: DSMC, March 1988. Describes in detail the role of testing in military contracting.

Duane, J. T. "Learning Curve Approach to Reliability Monitoring." *IEEE Transactions on Aerospace, vol. 2,* 1964. Describes the Duane model of reliability growth.

Dyllis, D. D. and Ebel, G. H. "Field Failure Return Program, The Missing Link," *Proceedings, 6th National Conference and Workshop, Environmental Stress Screening of Electronic Hardware (ESSEH).* Mt. Prospect, IL: Institute for Environmental Sciences, Nov. 12–15, 1990, pp. 18–24. Describes a program that helps designers and original-equipment manufacturers select quality parts by giving them data about manufacturing quality and field failures.

General Dynamics, Forth Worth Division. *Generic Integrated Maintenance Diagnostics Task 12.* Fort Worth, TX: Draft of February 19, 1990. Reports a study of current weapon-system diagnostic problems. Prioritizes these problems with respect to diagnostic impact. Categorizes problems as mechanical, software, power, etc. States causes of each problem. Describes a recommended or proposed way to avoid each problem in future weapon systems.

General Dynamics, Pomona Division. *Phalanx Close-In Weapon System TAAF Plan.* Pomona, CA: September 1988. Describes the TAAF plan for the Phalanx Close-In Weapon System.

Ginzberg, M. G. "Notes on Testing Real-Time System Programs." *IBM Systems Journal,* vol. 4, 1965, p. 68. Provides notes on testing software that must control a system in real time.

Guth, L. A. "Applicability of Low-Solids Flux." *Proceedings of the Singapore-U.S. Seminar on Chlorofluorocarbons,* September 17–19, 1990. Provides an example of how redesigning a process can reduce the likelihood of failures (i.e., soldering defects).

Higa, L. S. *Phalanx Close-In Weapon System Test Analyze and Fix (TAAF) Plan for Phalanx Block IR, TM 6-336-87-P-077D.* Pomona, CA: General Dynamics, September 13, 1988. Describes a successful application of the TAAF procedure.

International Electrotechnical Commission. *Programs for Reliability Growth.* Geneva, Switzerland: International Standard CEI IEC 1014, 1st ed., 1989. Documents the Crow procedure for projecting reliability to the end of reliability-growth testing. This procedure takes into account delays in implementing fixes.

Institute of Reliability Sciences (IES). *Glossary of Reliability Growth Terms.* Mount Prospect, IL: Institute of Environmental Sciences, 1989. Defines terms used in reliability-growth activities.

Kolcum, Edward H. "Navy Assesses Failure of First Trident 2 Underwater Launch." *Aviation Week & Space Technology,* March 27, 1989, pp. 18–19. Describes the Navy's assessment of the failure of the first underwater launch of the Lockheed Trident-2 missile, which blew apart after going out of control during the ignition stage.

Kolcum, Edward H. "Three Successful Launches Verify Design Fixes to Trident 2 D5 ICBM." *Aviation Week & Space Technology,* January 8, 1990, pp. 50–51. Describes in detail the two failures and three successful launches of Trident 2 D5 ICBM tests performed in 1989. Includes a comprehensive discussion on engineering design and fixes that eliminated the failures.

Lindsley, Michelle L. "Current Military Reliability Initiatives: An Overview." *Test Engineering & Management,* August/September 1989. Discusses various reliability initiatives and compares the reliability demonstration test with TAAF.

McDonnell Douglas Corporation. "Reliability Attainment." MDC, IRAD, vol. 3. Project

No. MDC Q0863-7. January 15, 1982, pp. 127450.03–127450.12. Describes efforts to improve the reliability techniques used to develop and produce military aircraft. Discusses operational-readiness problems.

Morrocco, John D. "Second Trident 2 Test Failure Points to Missile Design Flaw." *Aviation Week & Space Technology,* August 21, 1989, p. 26. Describes the second failure of the Navy's Trident-2 ballistic-missile test. Discusses the Navy's preliminary evaluation of the failure using the telemetry data.

Musa, John D., Aiannino, A., and Okumoto, K. *Software Reliability.* New York: McGraw-Hill, 1990. Includes methods for testing software to control and improve reliability.

Office of the Assistant Secretary of the Navy (Shipbuilding and Logistics). *Report of Survey of MK-15 Phalanx CIWS Program.* OASN (S&L), Reliability, Maintainability, and Quality-Assurance Directorate, September 14–16, 1988. Tells how a major acquisition program used the templates. Advocates putting the templates into the contract, determining the most capable contractor, and reducing risk. Suggests ways to improve acquisition.

Patterson, Douglas O. "The Navy and Reliability Growth: A Paradox at Best." *ITEA Journal,* vol. 9(3), 1988, pp. 27–31. Describes the benefits of TAAF concepts, their successful application to various military weapon systems, and various issues concerning a successful TAAF program. Discusses management policy, test articles, test environments, and test timing.

Perry, William P. *A Structured Approach To Systems Testing.* Wellesley, MA: QED Information Services, 1988. Tells how to establish test policy, develop test plan procedures, develop application system test plan, etc. Provides examples in software testing and describes how to evaluate results.

Phadke, M. S. *Quality Engineering Using Robust Design.* Englewood Cliffs, NJ: Prentice-Hall, 1989. Describes how robust-design techniques can be used to improve processes such as manufacturing. Includes the Taguchi method for designing experiments.

Priest, J. W. *Engineering Design For Producibility and Reliability.* New York: Marcel Dekker, 1988. Describes development testing, reliability growth, TAAF, integrated test-and-evaluation strategy, environmental and design-limit testing, life testing, accelerated life testing, operational testing, economics of testing, testability design requirements, levels of testing, testability approaches for electronic systems, and design techniques for testability.

Raytheon. *Transition from Development to Production.* Management Manual 956010, February 1985. Discusses issues concerning the 48 templates. Among these are technical risks, money phasing, design, testing, production, transition plan, facilities, and logistics support. Combines elements from both *Best Practices* (NAVSO P-6071) and *Transition from Development to Production* (DoD 4245.7-M).

Ricketts, M. P. "F/A-18 Hornet Reliability Challenge: Status Report." *Los Angeles: 1982 Proceedings of the Annual Reliability and Maintainability Symposium,* January 26–28, 1982. Reviews the major reliability program elements, provides the results of the Reliability Development Test Program (Test Analyze and Fix/Operational Mission Environment), and summarizes the results of the successful aircraft reliability demonstrations.

Robbins, N. B. "Tracking Reliability Growth with Delayed Fixes." *1990 Proceedings— Institute of Environmental Sciences,* 1990. Provides reliability-growth projections when corrective modifications are delayed.

Rogger, W. R. *F/A-18 Hornet: Reliability Development Testing.* Philadelphia: 1985 Proceedings of the Annual Reliability and Maintainability Symposium, January 22–24, 1985. Outlines the F/A-18 reliability program, the system requirements that drove it, to-date tests, and then-current results. Contents reliability development testing and reliability qualification testing. Mentions many surprises encountered during reliability improvement.

Sullivan, L. P. "Quality Function Deployment." *Quality Progress,* June 1986. Outlines the operational environment realistically modelled in reliability-development tests of F/A-18 avionics. Argues that contractors may not need to do reliability-qualification tests if reliability-development tests go well. Advocates dedicating equipment to reliability testing and early testing.

Von Alven, William H. *Reliability Engineering.* Englewood Cliffs, NJ: Prentice-Hall, 1964. Contains information on system effectiveness. Provides information on operational capability, i.e., the ability to counter a threat in terms of probability of kill; exchange ratios; operational availability, i.e., a system's ability to perform its intended use; and operational dependability, i.e., the probability that a system can complete its intended mission.

Walsh, L., Wurster, R., and Kimber, R. J., Eds. *Quality Management Handbook.* New York: Marcel Dekker, ASQC Quality Press, 1986. Describes Failure-Modes-and-Effects Analysis (FMEA) technologies for determining the causes of failures of hardware.

Wilbur, J. W. and Fuqua, Norman B. *Guidelines for DoD Reliability, Maintainability, and Safety Standards.* Rome, NY: Rome Air Development Center, Reliability Analysis Center, 1988. Describes various military specifications on reliability program, reliability assessment, major parts, maintainability program, maintainability assessment, and safety-related specifications.

Software Design and Software Test

Chapter

1

Introduction

To the Reader

Software design and test is a process that covers all the steps in software engineering. It involves two key Transition from Development to Production templates:[1] [2] Software Design and Software Test. These templates cover all activities in software development.

The templates, which reflect engineering fundamentals as well as industry and government expertise, were first proposed in the early 1980s by the Defense Science Board, under the chairmanship of Willis J. Willoughby, Jr. Their intent was to encourage everyone who is involved in the acquisition process to become aware of these templates and actually use them on the job.

This part on Software Design and Test is one part in a series of books written to help defense contractor engineers, government program managers, and contract administrators use the templates most effectively. These books are meant to stand-alone as references and textbooks for related courses.

Clustering several templates makes sense when their topics are closely related. For example, the templates in this book interrelate and occur iteratively within the software development process. Other templates, such as Design Reviews, relate to many other templates and are thus best dealt with individually in other books.

Over the past 10 or 15 years, software use has grown exponentially in every industry segment and government department in this country.

---

[1]*Department of Defense. September 1985. Transition from Development to Production.* DoD 4245.7-M.

[2]*Department of the Navy. March 1986. Best Practices: How to Avoid Surprises in the World's Most Complicated Technical Process.* NAVSO P-6071.

Our money systems, medical systems, communications systems, defense systems, and even our educational systems depend highly on computers. The success of these critical systems requires closely integrated hardware, firmware, and software; problems with any of these three can cause problems for the entire system. Increasingly, however, software has come under the heaviest fire from critics because of high cost, schedule slippage, and poor quality.

This part covers two *Transition from Development to Production* templates: Software Design and Software Test. In particular, this part covers all the steps in designing and testing software. These steps include related issues such as planning, maintenance, operations, and quality assurance. For more information about the Transition from Development to Production templates, see *Transition from Development to Production*[3] and *Best Practices: How to Avoid Surprises in the World's Most Complicated Technical Process.*[4]

Software System Cost

A generation ago, when computers first became part of business and government operations, the purchase price and operating cost of hardware were high; software expenditures were low.

One study (Figure 1) estimated that the amount of money spent for computerized systems in 1960 was 80% hardware and only 20% software. By 1980 the figures had inverted: 20% hardware and 80% software. The study further estimated that by 1990, the amount of money spent for software would likely be more than 90% of total systems' expenditures.[5]

As Figure 1 shows, money spent today on software in relation to hardware is increasing rapidly. In large, complex software systems, most of this increase can be attributed to the increasing cost of labor. Some systems, such as military control systems, air traffic control systems, and mainframe computer operating systems, require several thousand programmers working for years to produce more than one million lines of code. International Business Machines (IBM) recently reported that it takes 30 times more software code to support a shuttle mission for NASA than was required by the Apollo mission that took astronauts on their first trip to the moon.[6]

---

[3]Department of Defense.

[4]Department of the Navy.

[5]Fairley, Richard E. 1985. *Software Engineering Concepts.* New York: McGraw-Hill. 8.

[6]Joyce, Edward J. 1989. "Is Error-Free Software Achievable?" *Datamation* (February 15): 53.

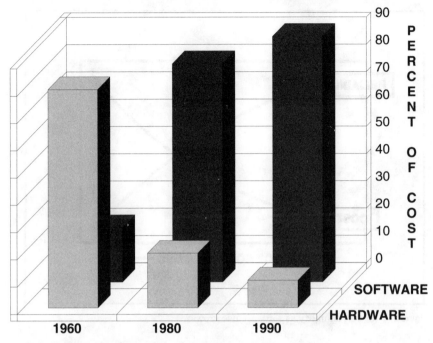

Figure 1 Trends in hardware and software costs.

With systems of such size and complexity, however, the cost of failure is extremely high; unfortunately, so is the cost of success. During the intense scrutiny of the space shuttle program after the 1986 disaster, the shuttle's software system was applauded for the high quality that was achieved, especially for realizing such a low rate of software defects. It is reported that for each thousand lines of code (KLOC) in the shuttle software, only 0.1 errors were detected after release. Industry defect rates average 80–100 times worse, with 8 to 10 errors per KLOC common. The achievement of such high quality, however, did not come cheaply. IBM reported that it cost NASA a total of $500 million to build the shuttle software system or about $1,000 per line of code.[7]

The cost of quality is a common criticism of software systems. Many observers complain that software systems are much too error-prone. It is claimed that the increased role of software in systems amplifies the costs, while it decreases the reliability.[8] (See Figure 2.)

---

[7]Joyce.

[8]DeMillo, Richard A. 1987. *Software Testing and Evaluation*. Menlo Park, CA: Benjamin/Cummings. vi.

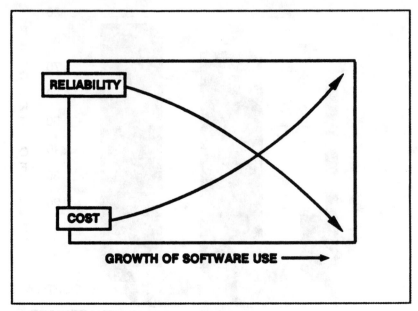

Figure 2 Cost vs. reliability as software use grows.

Cost and reliability concerns are further compounded by the belief that software systems are almost never delivered on time. Those that do meet schedules are then often criticized for not satisfying the system's specifications or the users' requirements. Some experts assert that accountability for software systems is so dispersed that development groups cannot learn from their own errors and thus cannot improve future efforts.

Software Risk Items

Cost and reliability are not the only technical risks in a software project. A leading software expert, Barry Boehm, has identified ten top software risk items (Table 1).[9] The items include not only budgets and performance shortfalls, but other concerns such as user needs and poor requirements.

---

[9]Boehm, Barry. 1989. *Risk Management Techniques*. Presentation at AT&T Bell Laboratories, Holmdel, NJ, May 3.

TABLE 1   Top Ten Software Risk Items

Risk item
Personnel shortfalls
Unrealistic schedules and budgets
Developing the wrong software functions
Developing the wrong user interface
Gold plating
Continuing stream of requirements changes
Shortfalls in externally-furnished components
Shortfalls in externally-performed tasks
Real-time performance shortfalls
Straining computer science capabilities

Keys to Success

NASA did achieve excellent software quality in the space shuttle project, but at a very high cost. Clearly, few other government agencies or companies can afford that cost, yet all organizations that produce software require good quality. There are five keys to success (Figure 3) that not only ensure good quality software, but also lower software costs and reduce the mentioned risks. These five keys are: Plan, Organize, Communicate, Control, and Measure. These five principles are illustrated throughout the Procedures and Application chapters of this part.

Plan

Plan for a project's entire life cycle, not just coding. Production and maintenance are critical stages of a project often completely overlooked. Sometimes, those two phases alone ultimately account for more than half of the total effort devoted to a project.

Plan the approach to be used in development. Various methodologies exist—which is best for the given project? What tools and techniques make sense?

Plan for software verification and validation throughout the entire development life cycle. Consideration of verification and validation methods, tools, techniques, and staff is important for building quality into the system from the start.

Organize

Organize the project based upon the architecture and the development

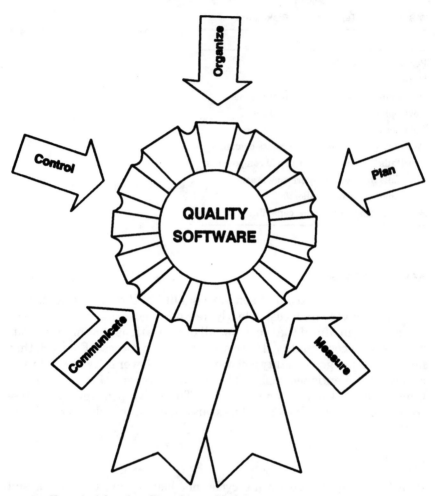

Figure 3 Key principles of quality software development.

method. Ensure that project accountability is clear.

Organize an appropriate team. Consider technology, skill levels, diversity of knowledge, and leadership.

Communicate

Communicate project goals, objectives, guidelines, milestones, and status with all team members. For large teams, a consistent method of timely communication is critical.

Communicate with users as appropriate for the project. Many experts believe that too much communication is better than too little.

Control

Control the changes to all aspects of the system, document the changes, and communicate them. Formal methods of configuration control are available and should be used.

Measure

Measure the progress of the system and communicate the status—both good and bad—with the project team regularly. Accurate measurements are essential for good management of software development projects.

Measure to improve the process, not to penalize individuals. Statistics about productivity, for example, may be collected from individuals, but results should be published for the group as a whole. Thus, you remove the fear of incrimination (being identified as a contributor to poor productivity) which can produce often unreliable measurements.

2

Procedures

The importance of high-quality, reliable software cannot be overemphasized. A disciplined approach, with consideration given to best practices, helps ensure success.

Software design and test encompasses a broad range of activities, often referred to collectively as *software engineering*. This term is used frequently throughout Part 2.

This Procedures chapter describes an eight-step process for developing a software system. For ease of discussion, the steps in this Part 2 are presented in sequence. In software development, however, these steps are highly interrelated. They frequently overlap and occur iteratively, depending upon the software development model chosen. See Figure 4.

Chronological Steps

Below is a sequence of steps that often occurs in software engineering.

Step 1 involves establishing a clear definition of the software system. The objectives are to assess user needs and determine the feasibility of the system.

Step 2 describes critical elements of software planning. It addresses issues relating to team, cost, life cycle, documentation, design reviews, change control, metrics, and tools.

Step 3 examines important factors involved in software requirements definition. Key aspects for determining *what* the system will accomplish are identified.

Step 4 involves software system design and *how* the software will meet the requirements. It describes preliminary design, system architecture, hardware architecture, software architecture, and detailed software design.

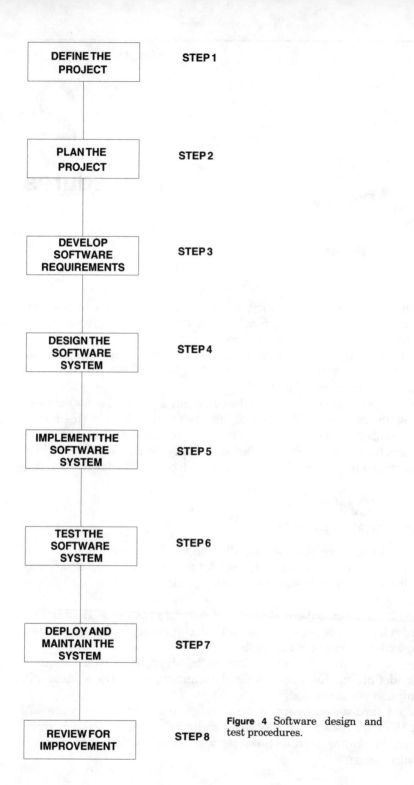

Figure 4 Software design and test procedures.

Step 5 discusses the software implementation. Use of structured programming techniques, coding standards, and code walkthroughs and inspections are highlighted.

Step 6 examines the critical issues involved in testing a software system. Module testing, integration testing, and system testing methods and techniques are discussed.

Step 7 details important aspects involved with installing a software system, operating it, and maintaining it.

Step 8 involves a review of both the software product and the development processes with a goal of continual improvement. Specific metrics and techniques are discussed.

Step 1: Define the Concept

The first step necessary in software development is a clear definition of the concept, opportunity, or problem, together with its proposed solution. For embedded software systems, look for the definition in the design requirements or in the design reference mission profile; with systems that are software only, that may not be the case.

Writing a clear definition of the major functions of a software system at the outset is critical. This information may have been provided by the customer, or it may be developed in-house. *Design to Reduce Technical Risk* provides details for embedded systems. See Figure 5 for an overview of the tasks involved in concept definition.

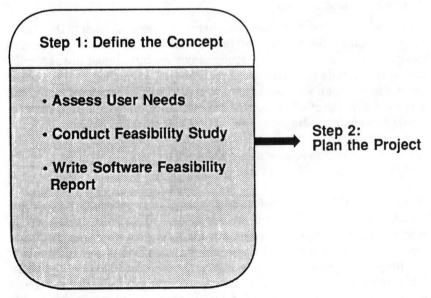

Figure 5 Concept definition.

Assess user needs

Before undertaking a software development project, examine whether the software will address user needs. User needs encompass not only what the user *says* he or she needs, but also what is not stated. For example, a user may complain about how unreadable a document is when in actuality if the system were designed more logically, complex user documentation would not be required.

Either the customer or the software development team undertakes a *software needs analysis*. This is a formal process of studying the intended users of the software and how they presently do their jobs, and then attempting to project how the job will be performed with the new system. Techniques recommended for gathering data about the users include:

- user surveys
- user interviews
- observation of the users and the tasks associated with the current situation or the new system
- actual execution of the user's job as it relates to the new system

It is important to realize that a new system may significantly change users' jobs. The analysis of user needs must include new user tasks and activities.

Conduct a feasibility study

A *feasibility study* determines whether a software solution to the stated problem is feasible, that is possible, practical, and viable. The factors examined during a feasibility study may vary but almost always, critical issues include performance, reliability, and maintainability. Other factors include: an assessment of the complexity of a software solution; a review of state-of-the-art software technology pertaining to the proposed system; an estimation of resources required to develop, operate, and maintain the software; the regulatory or policy controls that will affect software development and operation; and economic analysis including an estimation of the payback period.

Who conducts the software feasibility study? The persons responsible for a software feasibility study should be skilled software systems engineers who are highly proficient in conducting the required analyses. Communication between the systems engineers and the customer of the proposed system is important. Customers must be completely satisfied with the outcome of this process. They must believe their needs are understood and addressed. A wrong turn can be corrected quickly and at very little expense compared to the consequences of changes in subsequent stages of software development.

Software prototyping and system simulation may be helpful tools in determining feasibility. These techniques are discussed later in this part.

Write a software feasibility report

The outcome of the concept definition period should be a formal Software Feasibility Report. This must be a clear, concise statement of why a software development effort is proposed. The quality depends upon the amount of time available as well as the size of the project. The report should include the high-level expectations of the software, an analysis of the risks associated with the software development, unresolved software development issues, and all assumptions made during the feasibility study. The report should be written in terms easily understood by the customer, and a formal design review of the report should be conducted. (Chapter 3: Application includes a detailed description of the contents of a Software Feasibility Report.)

The end of the concept definition period marks a major milestone. Based on the Software Feasibility Report, management must make a "go" or "no-go" decision. If a decision is made to continue development efforts, funding is made available to begin detailed analysis activities and the development of the software requirements.

Step 2: Plan the Project

Effective planning for software development involves much more than planning for coding. In fact, coding is one of the least critical concerns in the early stages of a software project. The important early development issues are:

- choose and train a competent team
- define a software cost estimation model
- choose a software life cycle model
- define a software documentation methodology
- define requirements for reviews, inspections, and walkthroughs
- define a software change control management scheme
- define appropriate software metrics
- choose appropriate software tools

Address and define these tasks during the early stages of a software project. (See Figure 6.)

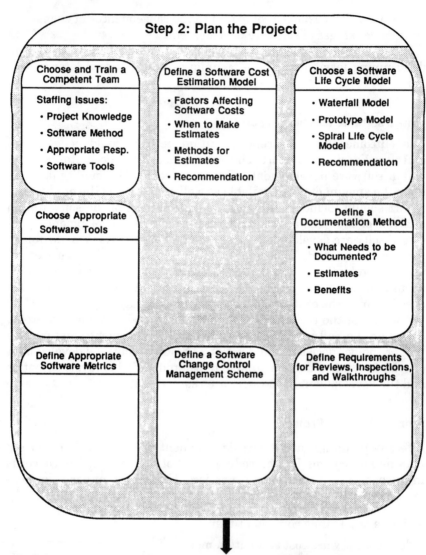

Step 3: Develop the Software Requirements

Figure 6 Project planning.

Choose and train a competent team

The skill levels and training needs of a software development team are frequently overlooked during the early phases of a project. Lack of attention to these important issues often results in more time and money being required for a project than originally anticipated.

A number of studies show wide differences between the abilities of programmers. In one study, a particular programming problem was presented to each of several experienced programmers. They were assigned to design, develop, and test their solutions; programmer activities were then measured and compared.[10] Eliminating the best and worst cases, the study found that a variation of 5-to-1 in programmer productivity is normal. The results showed, however, that depending on the activity, variations much higher than 5-to-1 also could be found. For example, comparisons of the times required to debug the programs exhibited a 28-to-1 variation, and the execution times of the finished programs varied by as much as 8-to-1.

The skill levels of a project's programming staff can have a significant effect on productivity and schedule. Since software development is labor intensive, it is important that management address the skill levels and training needs of all project team members: analysts, planners, systems engineers, designers, programmers, testers, documenters, and trainers.

Staffing issues to consider.   Several issues that management needs to consider when choosing and training the software development team are: project knowledge, software methodology, and appropriate responsibilities.

- *Project Knowledge.* Is there project-specific and application-specific expertise on the project team? Is this project similar to others in the organization, or is this project so different that an overall project training course needs to be developed for team members? What level of detail is needed in the training? Who will develop it? Who should attend?

- *Software Methodology.* What is the level of understanding on the team about software methodologies in general, and about how to choose the methodology appropriate for this project? Are there particular aspects of the project that require one methodology over another? Will any specialized training related to software methodology be required?

- *Appropriate Responsibilities.* Are the right people trained in the right skills? Are the systems analysts knowledgeable about how to work with users to gather data and information necessary to develop an accurate set of system requirements? Do the systems analysts

---

[10]Fairley 65.

know what a good system requirement is? Do the programmers know effective techniques for writing efficient code or for debugging a software program? Is the system test group trained in the art of software testing? If some members of the team will be asked to do multiple tasks, is cross-training planned?

Define a software cost estimation plan

The amount of money associated with software costs in this country today staggers the imagination. A report estimated that in 1980, software costs were $40 billion annually—or approximately two percent of the U.S. Gross National Product! A more recent study by the Electronic Industries Association showed that in 1985 the U.S. Defense Department alone spent approximately $11.4 billion on mission critical software costs and predicted that costs would grow to $36 billion by 1995.[11]

In an industry with such high costs and such rapid growth rates, one would think that sound, sophisticated tools for producing accurate and verifiable cost estimates would be available. In reality, cost estimation for software projects is far from an exact science. Cost estimation frequently emerges as management's most difficult and error-prone responsibility. According to research by Capers Jones, a software industry expert, manual calculation of software cost estimates can be off by 50 to 150 percent.[12]

Factors affecting software costs.   There are numerous factors affecting software costs. Management must be aware of these factors and must consider their effects when planning and estimating costs for a software development project.

Listed below are six of the most important factors affecting software costs.

- *Project Size.* The most obvious software cost factor is the size of the project; that is, the ultimate number of lines of code that need to be written to meet the requirements of a system. This factor, however, cannot be used by itself to estimate resources since required lines of code is variable depending upon the programming language used, the use of code generators, and the skill of the programmer.

---

[11]Boehm, Barry W. and Philip N. Papaccio. 1988. "Understanding and Controlling Software Costs." *IEEE Transactions on Software Engineering.* vol. 14, no. 10 (October). 1462.

[12]Contese, Amy. 1988. "Estimating Tools Reap 85% Accuracy, Some Say." *Computerworld* (November 14): p. 33.

- *Product Complexity.* The type and complexity of the software is a significant cost factor. Software projects are often categorized into three basic types: application programs (for example, business data processing); utility programs (for example, language compilers or debuggers); and system-level programs (for example, operating systems or real-time systems). Several years ago, Brooks stated that it is three times more difficult to write utility programs than it is to write application programs and nine times more difficult to write system-level programs.[13]

- *Required Reliability.* Software reliability should be a significant consideration in project plans. A study conducted on more than 60 software development projects and 25 software maintenance projects showed that, if all other factors were equal, the cost of developing software in which reliability was critical would be almost twice as much as developing software with only minimal reliability requirements. The study further showed, however, that the costs of maintenance were reversed, with the minimally reliable systems more costly to maintain.[14]

- *Level of Technology.* Items that increase or reduce the productivity of team members on a software project ultimately cause proportional cost increases or reductions. The level of technology used on a project is one factor that can substantially affect productivity. Level of technology includes analysis and design tools and techniques, the programming language, debugging aids, testing tools, simulators, text editors, and database management systems. Management must be aware of available software technologies and plan for their use.

- *Product Novelty.* Whenever a new project is introduced into a software organization, there are various unknowns that can produce inaccurate software cost estimates. For example, the programming group has experience developing spread sheet applications, while the new project involves real-time transactions. The introduction of different programming languages, operating systems, or computer processors can also substantially effect cost estimates.

  In the planning stage, management should determine if there are significant differences between previous software projects and the one under development. If such differences exist, previous cost estimation techniques should be adjusted to compensate for all new project factors.

---

[13]Brooks, Jr., Frederick P. 1979. *The Mythical Man-Month: Essays on Software Engineering* Reading, MA: Addison-Wesley. 4–6.

[14]Boehm and Papaccio, 1463.

More recently, Fairley noted the differences in programmer productivity for these three types of projects. He states, as a general rule of thumb only, the typical figures for lines of code that can be produced per programmer day (based on project complexity) are: 25 to 100 lines of code for an application program, 5 to 10 lines of code for a utility program, and less than one line of code per day for a system-level program.[15]

- *New vs. Reuse.* One method of controlling, and often reducing, the costs of software projects is to reuse software components rather than to build new components. Experts claim that costs for reusable software generally average only 30 percent of the cost to build a new component.[16] Software reuse, however, must be considered early in a project's life cycle and it must be planned. Force-fitting "old" software for the sake of reuse can end up costing a project much more than originally estimated.

Other factors also affect software costs and must be carefully reviewed when estimating the people, time, and computer resources needed for each phase of a software project. Table 2 lists 18 other important software cost factors.

When to make software cost estimates. The first cost estimates for a software development project are generally required during a product's feasibility stage. Estimates are very rough at this point since the understanding of the problem is still usually high-level. It is important that initial cost estimates are not cast in concrete. Instead, they should be reviewed and updated, if necessary, when each of the following mile-

TABLE 2   Other Software Cost Factors

Problem understanding	Appropriate goals
Stability of the requirements	Design stability
Available development time	Number of lines of code
Use of notations	Management skill
Change control	Team ability
Required skills	Team communication
Training	Staff build-up
Personnel turnover	Morale
Concurrent hardware development	Equipment delays

---

[15]Fairley, 17.

[16]"Managing Software Development: Solving the Productivity Puzzle." 1985. *Course Moderator's Guide*. New York: John Wiley.

stones is completed: the System Requirements Review, the Software Requirements Review, the Software Preliminary Design Review, and the Software Detailed Design Review. Additionally, maintenance cost estimates should be reviewed upon system delivery and revised if necessary.

Methods for estimating software costs. There is no single prescribed method or technique for estimating costs for every size and type of software project being developed today. Some of the common techniques, with their advantages and disadvantages, are:

- *Expert Estimation.* Expert estimation is a technique in which one or more highly experienced people use expert judgment, past experiences, and an understanding of the current problem to develop a cost estimate.

  Advantages: Projections can be developed quickly; better for determining interactions and exceptional circumstances.

  Disadvantages: Results are only as valid as the expert's experiences and biases; data is rarely verifiable.

- *Project Similarity.* This technique involves estimating costs by comparing similarities and differences for the proposed new project and past projects. (Expert judgment is not usually expected.) Cost estimates are then extrapolated.

  Advantages: This method can be very accurate, quick, and quite reliable.

  Disadvantages: No two projects or systems are exactly alike.

- *Lines of Code Estimation.* With this method, the total number of lines of code to be developed for a project is first estimated, and then a cost figure is approximated based on the resources (human and machine) needed to produce the estimated amount of code.

  Advantages: It is an easy method to use for quick estimates.

  Disadvantages: No clear relationship exists between lines of code and what the customer wants to buy and only a gross relationship exists between lines of code and the time it takes to produce them. Accurate estimates of lines of code is difficult and lines of code vary by programmer and project complexity.

- *Cost Estimation Models.* In recent years the software industry has seen the emergence of a number of cost estimation models. These models first require the identification (or estimation) of specific information about a project, mostly related to the software cost factors listed earlier. The information is then fed into the model (many are automated software tools) and estimates of development time and personnel resources are calculated. Some of the models even provide recommended staffing levels for various phases of the project.

Several of the most frequently used cost estimation models for software are: COCOMO, (the COnstructive COst MOdel developed by B. Boehm of TRW); SPQR/20 (from Software Productivity Research, Inc.); Function Points (developed by A. Albrecht at IBM); and SLIM (developed by L. Putnam of Quantitative Software Management). Chapter 3: Application includes a description of COCOMO cost estimating.

Advantages: Estimates are consistent internally; results are repeatable.

Disadvantages: Accuracy based on broad industry data is suspect; estimates are calibrated to data from the past that may not be accurate in the future.

Cost estimation recommendation. Since each of the available cost estimation methods has advantages and disadvantages, many experts recommend using a combination of techniques to develop several estimates that can be compared and consolidated into one.

Each software development organization should also collect and maintain actual cost data about the projects it develops. This historical data can then be used as a basis for determining cost for new projects and for calibrating cost models to the particular environment in which a project will be developed.

Choose a software life cycle model

Critical activities in the planning stage of software development are choosing and defining a life cycle model for the project. In software development, the term life cycle covers all aspects of development—from the earliest phases of the project's definition through installation, operation, and maintenance.

Three commonly used software development life cycle models are: the waterfall model, the prototype model, and the spiral model. Each of these methods is discussed briefly below.

Waterfall model. The waterfall model for software development is the basis for many software development projects in industry and government today. This model was first acknowledged in the late 1960s and early 1970s as an excellent tool for identifying and classifying the various phases in the life cycle of a software project. The phases identified include: feasibility, requirements, design, implementation, test, operations, and maintenance. The term "waterfall" implies that phases flow neatly and logically from beginning to end, from one phase into the next logical phase.

Given the nature of software projects, however, it is almost impossible for a project to finish one phase completely before moving on to the next as the term "waterfall" might suggest. The basic model has therefore evolved to look like Figure 7, with both forward and backward flows. The model includes verification and validation activities for each phase, with feedback to previous phases. The primary emphasis of the waterfall model is a systematic, disciplined, phased approach to software development.

Prototype model. A prototype reduces overall program risk by early modeling of an unclear aspect of the project such as user needs or available technology. In software development, the prototype life cycle model is based upon the use of various system prototypes throughout the development process.

Prototypes are commonly used to demonstrate a critical aspect of the system to users or to refine the users' needs. User interface requirements (screens, interface languages, and reports) are frequently uncovered using a prototype.

Technical risk reduction. Another reason for using prototypes is to reduce technical risk. A prototype is used to investigate or prove a particular technical aspect of a system. Some examples:

- Can performance and response time be improved? Can key algorithms be optimized?

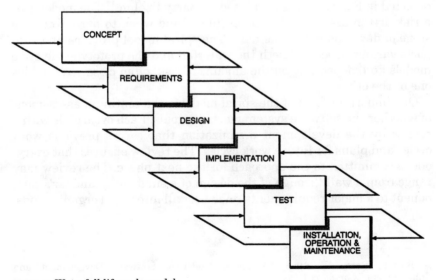

Figure 7 Waterfall life cycle model.

- Can the required response time be achieved using a new hardware or software component? Will the chosen component be compatible with the system?

- Can a new database management system adequately handle the load of the targeted system?

Implementation of the basic prototype life cycle model can follow two very different approaches, concentrating on: *system exploration* or *system evolution*. Project management and the project team must clearly define the preferred approach.

The first approach, *system exploration,* is one in which the prototype development is purely for exploration and data gathering. Once that job is done, the prototype is "thrown away." Experts who encourage this method claim that lessons learned from the prototype activity allow developers to "do it right" the next time and therefore produce a much higher quality product.

The second approach, *system evolution,* is often also called the *evolutionary development model* or the *successive versions model.* In this approach, prototypes are continually enhanced to provide more and more detail and refinement of the users' requirements for the software. Each succeeding version of a prototype is an improvement of a previous one. This technique provides quality checkpoints throughout the product development cycle.

Spiral model.   The spiral life cycle model for software development, as depicted in Figure 8, was developed by Barry Boehm.[17] The model uses a risk-driven assessment to determine if and when to move from one stage of development to the next. The spiral model provides and supports various aspects of both the waterfall and the prototype life cycle models and, depending on the amount of risk, often closely resembles one or the other.

One important facet of the spiral model is the continual assessment of whether the software system meets its goals. Each cycle ends with a review by the development organization that covers previous work cycles and plans for future work cycles. The review ensures that everyone is committed to the approach for the next phase. The review may range from a walkthrough of the design of a single programmer's component to a major requirements review for all interested organizations.

---

[17]Boehm, Barry W. 1988. "A Spiral Model of Software Development and Enhancement." *Computer* (May).

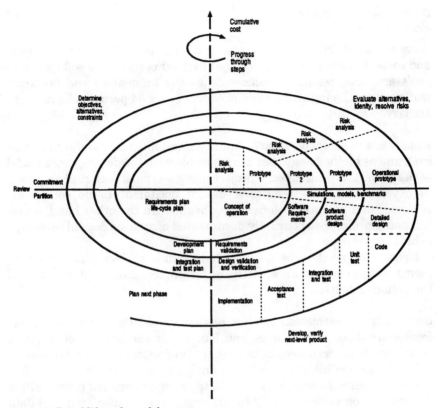

Figure 8 Spiral life cycle model.

If the software development fails to pass a review, the cycle or steps are repeated, or the process is terminated.

Life cycle model recommendation. A software life cycle model brings order and control to the development process. The model identifies specific activities that must occur and establishes unambiguous definitions for each stage of the process. No particular life cycle model is best for all software projects and, for some projects, a combination of several must be used. Most software experts believe that software development success does not necessarily depend on which specific model is chosen. Rather, what is important is that a model is chosen and defined and then clearly communicated to all project team members. If this is done well, and the model is understood, accepted, and followed by the team, then the flow of information on the project can be enhanced; project control becomes easier because it is well-defined. Ultimately, the product quality is improved.

Define a software documentation methodology

Software documentation accounts for a large part of a project's efforts and costs. Boehm has estimated that over 50 percent of a software project's activities result in documents as the immediate end products, while code is the immediate end product of only 34 percent of a project's activity.[18]

What needs to be documented?   Management must be careful to choose a document methodology that is compatible with the development model of the project. For instance, a project using a typical waterfall approach to development may require a design document to be completely reviewed and accepted before coding begins. On the other hand, a project using prototypes is usually documented after a successful prototype is built.

Items that need to be documented include project plans, requirements, system architecture, software design, test plans and results, and the actual code itself.

Documentation estimates.   Boehm has compared documentation rates from several software studies and found that the amount of software documentation for a project is roughly proportional to the number of delivered source instructions.[19] His analysis shows that for each 1,000 delivered source instructions (KDSI), the range of printed pages (PP) of documentation varied from 12 to 162 pages. Boehm also extracted data from the studies about the number of team-member hours (MH) required per page to write, review, and revise the documentation (excluding documentation design and planning). He estimates that:

for a small project and for the manuals of large projects   2 MH/PP

for the specifications and plans of a large project   4 MH/PP

Using 50 PP/KDSI as an average estimate of the number of pages of documentation and 3 MH/PP as an average estimate of the member hours per page of documentation, the calculation:

$$(3 \text{ MH/PP})(50 \text{ PP/KDSI}) = 150 \text{ MH/KDSI}$$
$$(\text{approximately 1 month})$$

shows that a software project requiring 1,000 lines of code needs one team-member a month for the documentation.

---

[18]Boehm, Barry W. 1981. *Software Engineering Economics.* Englewood Cliffs, NJ: Prentice-Hall. 488–489.

[19]Boehm, *Software Engineering Economics,* 571–575.

Benefits of documentation. Frequently, those involved with a software project question why so much documentation is required. Vincent, Waters, and Sinclair offer the following five reasons (the first three of which are from Frederick P. Brooks) that documentation is essential to the success of a software project:[20]

1. "Writing down decisions is essential: only when documented will gaps and inconsistencies appear, and all the hundreds of mini-decisions which must be made come into clear focus."

2. "Documentation communicates decisions to others and considerably lightens the manager's job of keeping everyone going in the same direction."

3. "Documentation offers the manager a data base and checklist—and periodic reviews will show the manager where he is and what changes in emphasis or shifts in direction are necessary."

4. "Documentation offers a clearly definable position—essential in demonstrating to the customer how requirements and specifications are being met, and how the project is evolving."

5. "Documentation provides a resource that may be used again in the development of future projects."

Another important consideration is that clearly written software documentation can greatly reduce the effort required to produce good user documents and training materials.

Define requirements for reviews, inspections, and walkthroughs

The goal of reviews, inspections, and walkthroughs within the software development project is to assess the design maturity and improve the quality of the workproducts (code and related documents). Effective design reviews and inspections are oriented toward error detection and the assessment of maturity. In contrast, management reviews concentrate on costs, schedules, and resources. Walkthroughs provide an overview of functions to be provided. They are especially useful when the design or code is complex.

The review and inspection team should have expertise in the key technical areas of the project, including systems analysis, software design, programming, and testing. Effective teams follow formal pro-

---

[20]Vincent, James and others. 1988. *Software Quality Assurance: Volume I, Practice and Implementation.* Englewood Cliffs, NJ: Prentice Hall. 90–92.

cedures, with well-defined roles and entry and exit criteria. Specific guidelines for individual reviewing time and meeting pace increase the chance of finding errors when the errors are easy to fix.

Although reviews and inspections take time and resources, they prove cost-effective—with savings of 10-to-1 if errors are found in requirements rather than in coding and with savings of 100-to-1 if errors are found in requirements rather than in the field.

Management support and commitment is vital. Time and resources for reviews and inspections must not be sacrificed when deadlines become tight. Managers should praise people for finding errors and ways to improve the process. (See the *Design to Reduce Technical Risk* for more details about these principles.)

Define a software change control management scheme

During the planning phase, a change control management system should be set up to capture changes made during the product life cycle. An effective change control system can identify, maintain, store, and retrieve changes and information on a product. Change management should be applied to all code and written outputs.

The change control system may be manual, automated, or a mix of manual and automated elements. The choice depends on the complexity of the software system, the availability of resources to develop the system, the frequency of required reporting, and the number of locations that must have access to the system. Features included in a configuration control system are:

- *Configuration Control.* This process establishes a frozen baseline and coordinates changes to the baseline. A baseline is an intermediate product, designated at a milestone, and used as a basis for comparison to a future product. Changes must be approved before altering software and updating files. Changes should be visible to ensure developers work with the latest information. (Refer to *Design to Reduce Technical Risk* for more details.)

- *Configuration Identification.* This process defines and identifies versions of software components and systems (release or version numbers). Versions may be labeled to indicate development phases and customer releases.

- *Configuration Accounting.* This process enters potential solutions for defects. The configuration accounting system must provide feedback on the solutions to modification requests. When the defects are corrected, the files are automatically updated, but previous versions are kept. Developers may then review the reasons for the changes. Prior versions of the product may be restored, if necessary.

- *Configuration Auditing.* This process monitors the administrative and technical integrity throughout software development to improve the process continually. Experienced auditors, independent of the development efforts, establish baselines and implement metrics. They may also oversee the use of military specifications, development of standards, test planning, design reviews, error tracking, and tools certification.

Define appropriate software metrics

Software metrics measure various aspects of the software, with an eye toward eventual improvement of the final product (*outcome metrics*) or the development process (*process metrics*). The term "metric" means "measure." An ideal collection of metrics for software development has the following characteristics:

- measures the process from the requirements stage through delivery and use by the customer

- can be customized to suit small, medium, and large projects

- provides measures of software quality, accuracy, completeness, timeliness, and productivity that allow action to be taken early to correct any deficiencies

- provide guidelines on how to correct deficiencies as they arise

- pays off in results for the effort spent collecting, plotting, and interpreting the metrics

- includes both outcome and process metrics

Outcome metrics. Outcome metrics measure whether the final product has met customer needs. They are implemented after the product has been delivered. Customer needs often include quality, performance, availability, and cost. If quality is defined as the degree to which a product or service meets evolving customer expectations, then quality software meets customer expectations for performance, availability, and cost. Quality software is not only free from defects, it is also available on time, easy to use, and easy to maintain.

Outcome measures for software development usually measure software faults found internally and by customers. A fault occurs when the software fails to conform to requirements or fails to meet customer needs. The level of severity indicates the seriousness of the fault from the customer's point of view: interruption of basic service, degradation of basic service, inconvenience, and minor deficiencies of little consequence.

Examples of outcome metrics for software development. Examples of outcome metrics that measure quality, performance, timely availability, and customer satisfaction are:

- results of customer satisfaction surveys
- cumulative density of faults found internally and by customers from the start of system test to one year after release
- results of acceptance tests conducted in the customer environment
- timeliness of the documentation measured by the percentage of volumes shipped on the release date

Process metrics. Process metrics are related to outcome metrics, but give immediate feedback on the quality of the development process. Process metrics fine-tune the development process to achieve outcomes and are usually implemented *during* the process. Process metrics can be used to:

- track the progress of software development against milestones and estimates of completion
- measure the quality of the software
- evaluate the effectiveness of the reviews and inspections
- evaluate the effectiveness of the development team and management
- identify areas for improvement

Examples of process metrics for software development. Examples of process metrics are:

- *Requirements availability.* These metrics compare the rate of completion of the system requirements to the amount of completed development effort.
- *Change management.* These metrics measure the impact of major feature changes on baselined requirements. The goal is to identify the staff months associated with deleting features, adding features, or making major changes to features.
- *Fault detection profile.* This metric shows fault densities found in each development phase. Compare fault densities found early with those found later; compare projects of similar size and complexity. Remember that improvements to prevent design and coding errors

reduce errors there and in later testing phases. Earlier improve-ments (requirements, for example) increase error density early but reduce it in later phases (testing, for example). This metric also helps in defect analysis and root cause analysis.

- *Fault cause profile.* This metric shows the kinds of faults that occur often in each development phase. Steps can then be taken to avoid introducing these faults or to find them earlier. The data can also be used to see whether process improvements are actually working to reduce and prevent faults.

Refining the metrics.   Projects get the most benefit from metrics when the metrics are refined based on actual use. As the project team collects historical data on outcome and process, they can set objectives and guidelines based on their own situation and past performance. The payoffs will be seen quickly.

Choose appropriate software tools

In recent years, there has been considerable research in the area of soft-ware engineering. Much of that research has produced new tools and techniques whose proponents claim improved programmer productivity and decreased overall system development time frames. Unfortunately, many of the tools available today (for example, code generators, applica-tion generators, report writers, library managers, test case generators) focus on later stages of system development. Software analysis and soft-ware design tend to be performed much as they have been for the past 10 to 25 years, although some of the standard techniques have now been enhanced with automated "companion" tools.

One example often cited is Computer-Aided Software Engineering (CASE) which is discussed below. There have also been extensions to many of the classical analysis and design techniques to accommodate real-time systems development such as state-transition modeling and control flow analysis. Advances have been made, however, using expert systems technology to improve systems development, but many of these systems remain only experimental or are limited to a very nar-row selection of software systems.

CASE.   CASE is the general name for a wide range of automated prod-ucts used in the development of software. Each CASE product contains a set of tools which are utilized at different stages throughout the development activity. In the best products, all the tools are closely inte-grated and provide a complete development environment. The base set of tools for a CASE product usually contains

- a tool for specifying the requirements of a system
- a tool for determining system design
- a data dictionary for storage of the system's data information
- a code generator
- a test generator

Selecting and using a CASE system requires careful planning. Although most CASE products are user-friendly, their effective use still requires substantial training and experience. This is especially true when the CASE product supports a new development methodology.

Step 3: Develop the Software Requirements

Following concept definition, a software project enters the software requirements or requirements analysis phase. The objective is a more specific understanding of *what* the completed software system will do, instead of *how* the system will do it (which is discussed in Step 4). The tasks involved in developing software requirements are shown in Figure 9.

Requirements vs. feasibility

The two major differences between the requirements phase and the feasibility phase are:

- By the requirements phase, a decision has been made to continue with development; the feasibility phase lacks that assurance.
- The requirements phase is concerned with detailed specifications; the feasibility phase is appropriately high-level.

Who conducts the software requirements analysis?

Software systems analysts develop the software requirements with participation from any of the following: hardware specialists, communications specialists, lead programmers, database specialists, and documentation specialists. Additional key participants should be the customer and users of the system. Their subject-matter expertise is critical to the success of the future system. Lack of either group's involvement at this stage often results in substantial system rework.

The Software Feasibility Report (from Step 1) is a primary input into the analysis and development of the software requirements. In fact,

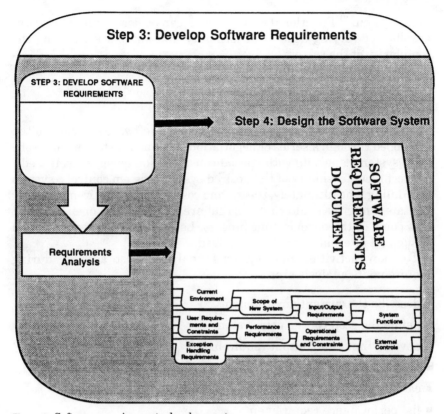

Figure 9 Software requirements development.

many of the aspects of the software system that were analyzed during concept definition will be revisited during requirements. The analysts refine the high-level system objectives into a prioritized, detailed, and quantifiable set of conditions. Note that the system requirements developed and documented during this period become the basis for the development of the overall software system design, the software system test plan, and the software user-acceptance test plan (see Steps 4–7). It is critical, therefore, that requirements be complete, explicit, and contain measurable acceptance criteria.

Software requirements document

The software requirements document should be developed to describe both what the system does and what it does not do. Too often, it is tacitly assumed that anything left out of the document will not be added to the system.[21] Functional requirements can be documented in text or graphics of varying degrees of formality and automation suiting the complexity of the system.

Key aspects of the software requirements specification

The final prioritized set of requirements for a software system is often developed through a series of negotiations between customers and software systems analysts with special consideration given to user needs, the technical feasibility of the desired system, system controls, system scheduling, and ultimately, the system cost. Various requirements may be stated in terms of alternatives that are purposely left open-ended at this point in the development process. Later, during software system design, all alternatives will be resolved.

Ten key activities that systems analysts must address during requirements analysis are:

- describe the current environment
- define the scope of the new system
- develop input and output requirements
- define the system's functions
- catalog user requirements and constraints
- list performance requirements
- itemize operational requirements and constraints
- identify maintenance requirements
- specify external controls
- develop exception handling requirements

Describe the current environment.   A new system often replaces an existing system or automates tasks currently performed manually. In either case a detailed study of the current environment should be completed. This study should give special attention to user activities and to the flow of data in the environment.

Define the scope of the new system.   An important activity in requirements analysis is to define clearly the scope and limits of the new sys-

---

[21]Quirk, W. J., ed. 1985. *Verification and Validation of Real-Time Software.* New York: Springer-Verlag. 23.

tem. Kirk urges analysts to "stretch the limits of the system to their natural boundaries."[22]

The requirements document should detail the scope of the new system and identify related activities that will not be part of the new system. This approach highlights these items and clarifies the system's limitations.

Define the system's functions.   A system's functions are those processes that occur to transform the identified inputs into the required outputs. The system is designed and implemented based on these functions.

System functions should be described logically rather than physically; by *what* should be done rather than *how*.[23] This is due to the volatility of the requirements. New aspects of the system are discovered frequently, impelling frequent changes to the requirements. It is better to tie functionality to implementation in the design step when volatility has decreased.

Develop input and output requirements.   Each input and each output for the new system must be identified and described, including input source(s), and output destination(s). References to external interfaces must also detail their requirements. Feedback—where input is dependent on output—must be considered.[24] Although many input and output details are specified during requirements analysis, methods for implementing them are not, since that is a function of system design.

The following list of input and output attributes specifies aspects to explore:

- content
- format
- accuracy
- security
- known or predicted volumes
- peak periods

[22]Kirk, Frank. 1973. *Total System Development for Information Systems.* New York: John Wiley and Sons. 85.

[23]Davis, Alan. 1988."A Comparison of Techniques for the Specification of External System Behavior." Communications ACM (*September*).

[24]Wymore, A. Wayne. 1976. *Systems Engineering Methodology for Interdisciplinary Teams.* New York: John Wiley and Sons. 111–165.

- retention duration
- geographical considerations (example: time zones)

Catalog user requirements. Identifying the users of the new system and the associated requirements is a large part of the requirements effort. Necessary details include: who the users are, how many users, the users' skill levels, the training required for the new system, the stability of the user population, the type and amount of documentation needed, and geographical considerations. Special consideration may be required for external users, as opposed to internal users.

It is vital that users perceive the system as meeting their needs. This perception is separate from whether the system actually does meet their needs. Too often, users do not base appraisals either on how well-designed the system is or on how well-managed the development effort is, but rather on the adequacy of their interface to the system. This interface includes not only user-machine communications, but also ease of using the documents.[25]

List performance requirements

All system requirements must be measurable and must have associated acceptance criteria, especially when detailing the system performance expectations. Inadequate or unacceptable system performance is a primary ingredient of user dissatisfaction.

Performance requirements in particular should be bounded rather than open-ended and so prevent over- or under-design. Here is an example of an open-ended requirement:

Response time for task X must not exceed 5 seconds.

Given this requirement, several questions remain unanswered:

- What may the user expect as the normal or average response time? Is it 5 seconds or something less than 5 seconds?
- If average response time is less than 5 seconds, how much less?
- Should the system be designed for an average response time of 1 second with a response time not to exceed 5 seconds under stressful conditions?

To remove the ambiguity, a better statement of the response time requirement might be:

---

[25]Page-Jones, Meilir. 1988. *The Practical Guide to Structured Systems Design.* 2nd ed. Englewood Cliffs, NJ: Yourdon Press. 286.

Response time for task X under average load conditions for the system should be in the 2- to 3-second range.

During peak load periods, the response time must not exceed 5 seconds.

Optimizing the design for the 2- to 3-second response range can be very different from trying to design for the lowest possible response time. With the revised requirement, a designer has a specific design target and users and system testers have specific acceptance criteria. Note: Average load and peak load must be clearly defined in the requirements for this to be an effective response time requirement.

Any system, particularly real-time systems, may have many performance requirements. The success of the system hinges on the specificity of the requirements. Several aspects of a system for which performance attributes should be examined and described include:

- response time
- start-up time
- availability
- fault detection and recovery
- maintenance
- communications
- reliability

Itemize operational requirements. The requirements for a system's operations cover a broad range. In most development efforts, the hardware and software components are not chosen until the design phase. Specifications may cite a particular processor size (that is, mainframe, minicomputer, or microcomputer) or require compatibility with a particular system. The physical location of the new system may also pose constraints, and these must be documented. Additional requirements may include resource parameters: use of memory, disk storage, file size, conversion requirements (for replacement systems), data redundancy, processor redundancy, off-site storage, backup capability, and recovery capability.

Identify maintenance requirements. The requirements for a system's maintenance cover every aspect of the system. The basis for good itemized maintenance requirements is a well thought out maintenance concept that describes how and who will do the maintenance. The maintenance concept should cover both software and hardware maintenance. It should also separate maintenance tasks performed by the user from maintenance tasks performed by trained maintenance personnel. The maintenance requirements should cover items such as level and types of tests, backup capability and schemes, and routine and emergency maintenance procedures. The overall maintenance concept and requirements may significantly impact the system architecture and the actual software.

Specify external controls. Many systems being developed today must adhere to external controls placed on the system. These may include business or government regulations, environmental controls, safety controls, or even political and social controls. All such requirements must be clearly specified during system requirements analysis.

Develop exception handling requirements. The exception handling requirements of a system involve a definition of the actions to be taken when undesired events or conditions occur. In a critical system involving life-threatening situations, exception handling receives top priority. In such a case, requirements for damage control or confinement may need to be developed. In less critical systems, requirements are concerned with system or user error messages, or with exception reports. Analysts often create categories of exceptions and define error handling in terms of the severity of the error category.

Software requirements review

The final requirements specification documents for a software system must be formally reviewed and accepted in a Software Requirements Review. Those involved in the review include: customers, users, software analysts, hardware designers, software designers, hardware testers, software testers, and management.

Software requirements specifications, although accepted, are not valid until it is determined that the resulting software system can be built for a reasonable cost. This requires the development of one or more software designs, which is generally the next step in software development.

After the Software Requirements Review, the Software Requirements Document should be baselined and placed under change control. Additionally, system resource estimates and schedules for the software should be updated to reflect modifications resulting from the review.

Most large, complex projects can expect changes to the system's requirements as software development progresses. Proposed changes to the requirements must be closely monitored, however, since they have the potential for large rippling effects as the software system development matures. Accepted revisions to the requirements must be reflected in the requirements specifications documents and they must be quickly and clearly communicated to the entire development team so that resource adjustments, if necessary, can be managed and coordinated.

Step 4: Design the Software System

Once the requirements have been detailed and accepted, determine how the software system will accomplish its specified tasks. Software system design is the process of allocating and arranging the functions of the system so that it meets all specified requirements. See Figure 10.

Since several different designs may meet the requirements, alternatives must be assessed based on technical risks, costs, schedule, and other considerations. A design developed before there is a clear and concise analysis of the system's objectives can result in a system that does not satisfy the requirements of its customers and users. In addition, an inferior design can make it very difficult for those who must

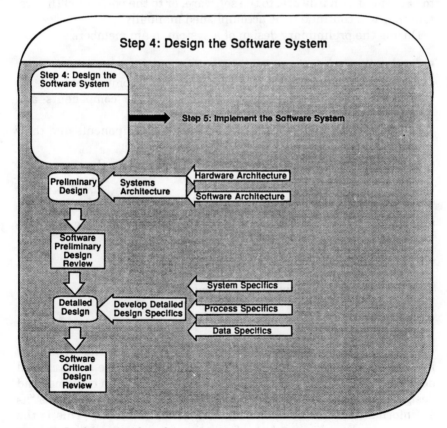

Figure 10   Implementing the software system.

later code, test, or maintain the software. During the course of a software development effort, analysts may offer and explore many possible design alternatives before choosing the best design.

Frequently, the design of a software system is developed as a gradual progression from a high-level or logical system design to a very specific modular or physical design. Many development teams, however, choose to distinguish separate design stages with specific deliverables and reviews upon completion of each stage. Two common design stages are *preliminary design* and *detailed design*.

Preliminary design

Preliminary or high-level design is the phase of a software project in which the major software system alternatives, functions, and requirements are analyzed. From the alternatives, the software system architecture is chosen and all primary functions of the system are allocated to the computer hardware, to the software, or to the portions of the system that will continue to be accomplished manually.

During the preliminary design of a system, team members

- develop the architecture
  system architecture—an overall view of system components
  hardware architecture—the system's hardware components and their interrelations
  software architecture—the system's software components and their interrelations
- investigate and analyze the physical alternatives for the system and choose solutions
- define the external characteristics of the system
- refine the internal structure of the system by decomposing the high-level software architecture
- develop a logical view or model of the system's data

This list is not all-inclusive or in any special order.

Develop the architecture

The architecture of a system describes its parts and the ways they interrelate. Peters notes that the lack of a clear, concise architectural description for a system makes communication between customer and designer difficult. An effective system architecture, however, acts "as an information pipeline at the highest conceptual level." This is the first step in the refinement of information from concept to implementation.[26] Like blueprints for a building, there may be various software architectural descriptions, each detailing a different aspect. Each architecture document usually includes a graphic and narrative about the aspect it is describing.

The *system architecture* shows the system hardware, software, and human aspects and the interfaces among them. A high-level system architecture is vital in a large, complex system, especially when functions are performed on different computers at different locations. It presents the overall system concept, enables understanding of the large issues, and helps uncover key areas of risk.

A system functional model is usually included as part of a system's architecture. It identifies the system's high-level functions and their interrelationships, external interfaces, input data sources, system outputs, and output destinations. The model also depicts the system's functional allocation—the allocation of functions to either the users or the system itself.

Primary considerations during system architecture development are the system's performance, cost, and reliability requirements as well as any technological and developmental constraints. Specific goals for the system design may also be identified. For instance, one goal may be to design a system so that the human interface is minimized. Another goal may be to create a system that will be easy to maintain in the future. Finally, a design goal frequently considered today is that of software reusability—either reusing previously developed software, or developing a new system whose software can be easily reused in the future.

A *hardware architecture* for a software system identifies the number, type, and location of items such as:

- processors (for example, personal computers, minicomputers, mainframes)
- storage, back-up, and recovery facilities
- end-user terminals (for example, display terminals, hand-held portable terminals)
- printers and output devices
- administrative and operator terminals
- protocol converters
- communications links (among processors and from terminals to processors)

---

[26]Peters, Lawrence J. 1981. *Software Design: Methods & Techniques*. New York: Yourdon Press. 44.

The development of a hardware architecture can help to highlight possible communications bottlenecks, capacity problems, and performance problems. It can also be very helpful in verifying the fault-tolerance of a system.

The *software architecture* for a system describes the internal structure of the software system. It breaks high-level functions into sub-functions and processes and establishes relationships and interconnections among them. It also identifies controlling modules, the scope of control, hierarchies, and the precedence of some processes over others. Areas of concern that are often highlighted during the establishment of the software architecture include: system security, system administration, maintenance, and future extensions for the system.

Another aspect of the software architecture may be the allocation of resource budgets for CPU cycles, memory, I/O, and file size. This activity often leads to the identification of constraints on the design solution such as the number of customer transactions that can be handled within a given period, the amount of inter-machine communication that can occur, or the amount of data that must be stored.

The first software architecture model for a system is usually presented at a very high level with only primary system functions represented. An example of a high-level software architecture is presented in Figure 11. As design progresses through detailed design, the architecture is continually refined.

Choose physical solutions.   Unless a software system has been given a pre-defined physical solution, an activity called *environmental selection* occurs during the preliminary design of a system. This is the process of investigating and analyzing various technological alternatives to the system and choosing a solution based upon the system's requirements, the users' needs, and the results of the feasibility studies.

Aspects of a system that are generally selected at this time are: the hardware processing unit; computer storage devices; the operating system; user terminals, scanners, printers and other input and output devices; and the computer programming language.

In some cases, hardware and software items such as communications hardware and software, report writers, screen management systems, or database management systems are available "off-the-shelf." This is especially true for aspects of a system that have no specialized functionality or performance requirements. In other cases, unique requirements of the system may dictate the development of specific hardware and software items, specially designed for the system. The additional resources required to customize the system must be estimated and reviewed.

Define external characteristics.   Following the software system's functional allocation and physical environment selection, the details of the

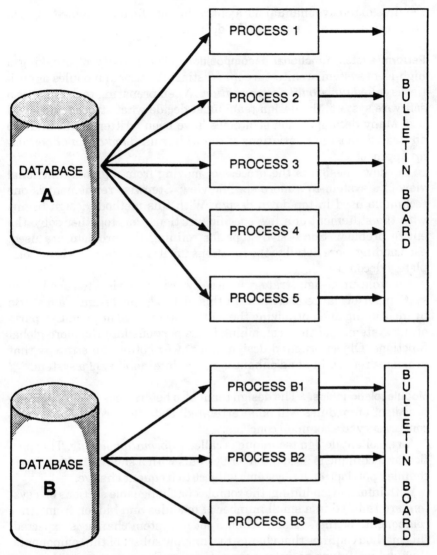

Figure 11 High-level software architecture example.

external or observable characteristics of a system can be developed. Included here would be terminal screen displays, report formats, error message formats, and interfaces to other systems.

A human factors engineer may be part of the design team concerned with the observable characteristics of a software system. This person specializes in the analysis of the human-machine interface. When a system's targeted users are novice computer users or when a system requires extensive manual data entry, human factors engineering can be a very important aspect of the design.

Perform system functional decomposition. The activity of breaking a high-level system architecture into distinct functional modules or entities is called *functional decomposition*. When preparing to decompose a software system, the design team must decide what strategy they will use. Many decomposition strategies have been written about and are advocated; most are variations of the widely used *top-down* or *bottom-up* approaches.[27]

Top-down design is the process of moving from a global functional view of a system to a more specific view. Stepwise refinement is one technique used in top-down design. With this method, design begins with the statement of a few specific functions that together solve the entire problem. Successive steps for refining the problem are used, each adding more detail to the functions until the system has been completely decomposed.

A bottom-up design strategy for a software system is often used when system performance is critical. In this method, the design team starts by identifying and optimizing the most fundamental or primitive parts of the system, and then combining those portions into the more global functions. Object-oriented design is a newer bottom-up strategy that promotes reusability and enhances the maintainability of a system.[28] [29]

Module relationships. The design team also determines how the decomposed set of modules will be interrelated. Data flow, control flow, and concurrency are common concepts.

An excellent design technique is called *information hiding*. This particular technique is used often for systems with a small number of very complex portions or for systems subject to frequent change.

With information hiding, the complex or changeable sections of a system are isolated in a small number of modules and hidden from other components of the system. When a lot of system change is expected, this method confines that change to a narrow subset of the components, thus aiding future maintenance activities. For a system with a few highly complex components, information hiding also aids system testing and debugging.

---

[27]Fairley, 161–163.

[28]Booch, Grady. 1986. "Object-Oriented Development," *IEEE Transactions of Software Engineering* (February).

[29]Meyer, Bertrand. 1988. *Object-Oriented Software Construction*. Englewood Cliffs, NJ: Prentice Hall.

Regardless of strategy, functional decomposition begins when the software architecture has been determined and usually continues throughout design. A difficult aspect of functional decomposition is knowing when it is done. Experts prefer erring on the side of decomposing too much and then combining low-level modules as needed to aid performance or enhance high-usage areas of the system.[30] They also suggest that a system should be decomposed until no subset of elements in the modules or entities can be used alone.

Data modeling. In almost every software system, quick access to data has a high priority. Therefore, how the system receives its data, how the system stores its data, and how data can be retrieved from the system are key factors to consider during system design. This is called *data modeling*. Data modeling and database design are usually the responsibility of highly skilled database experts who are part of the design team.

Requirements for data and data handling should have been developed during the requirements analysis activities (Step 3). When system design begins, the design team must have clear goals and objectives concerning data access performance, data volumes, data storage, data integrity, data reliability, and data security.

A *data flow diagram* is a common tool used during preliminary design of a software system to represent system processes and their data interconnections. With this tool and others, a logical view of all the data stores for the system is developed as well as a view of how data flows to various processes.

Data abstraction is a concept often used in data design. Much like information hiding, data abstraction hides the actual structure of data stores from the system's processes. With this method, a common set of database access routines is designed so that when the system is implemented, each process needs to know only these routines to access data.

Poor design of a system's data-handling activities can cause inefficient data access and poor system performance. Common problems caused by ineffective data design include:

- data corruption resulting from ineffective data file locking
- system or database deadlock resulting from the mishandled contention for access and release of common data files
- high usage of processing resources due to inefficient data access paths

---

[30]Fairley, 152.

Software preliminary design review

At the end of the preliminary design phase of a software system, a formal design review must be conducted. Customers of the system often mandate the Software Preliminary Design Review. The review examines design rationale and design assumptions, along with all the other preliminary design aspects mentioned above, to ensure that the resulting software system will meet the stated requirements. Since user manuals and software test plans develop in parallel with the software design activities, these items may also be considered for examination during the preliminary design review, or they may be reviewed separately. Particular attention should be given to the high-priority aspects of the system such as performance, security, maintainability, and system recovery.

The results of the Software Preliminary Design Review should provide management with enough information to decide whether to continue the software development effort. Acceptance or rejection of particular design alternatives may also mean that cost estimates need to be reviewed and revised before further work on the system is approved. See *Design to Reduce Technical Risk* for details.

Detailed design

Detailed design or low-level design determines the specific steps required for each component or process of a software system. Responsibility for detailed design may belong to either the system designers (as a continuation of preliminary design activities) or to the system programmers.

Information needed to begin detailed design includes: the software system requirements, the system models, the data models, and previously determined functional decompositions. The specific design details developed during the detailed design period are divided into three categories: for the system as a whole (*system specifics*), for individual processes within the system (*process specifics*), and for the data within the system (*data specifics*). Examples of the type of detailed design specifics that are developed for each of these categories are given below.

Detailed design examples.   System specifics:

- physical file system structure
- interconnection records or protocols between software and hardware components
- packaging of units as functions, modules or subroutines
- interconnections among software functions and processes

- control processing
- memory addressing and allocation
- structure of compilation units and load modules

Process specifics:

- required algorithmic details
- procedural process logic
- function and subroutine calls
- error and exception handling logic

Data specifics:

- global data handling and access
- physical database structure
- internal record layouts
- data translation tables
- data edit rules
- data storage needs

Detailed design tools

Various tools such as flowcharts, decision tables, and decision trees are common in detailed software design. Frequently, a structured English notation for the logic flow of the system's components is also used. Both formal and informal notations are often lumped under the term *pseudocode*. This is a tool generally used for the detailed design of individual software components. The terminology used in pseudocode is a mix of English and a formal programming language. Pseudocode usually has constructs such as "IF ..., THEN ...," or "DO ... UNTIL ...," which can often be directly translated into the actual code for that component. When using pseudocode, more attention is paid to the logic of the procedures than to the syntax of the notation. When pseudocode is later translated into a programming language, the syntactical representation becomes critical.

Level of detailed design.   A question frequently asked about detailed design is, "What level of design should be achieved?" As with other aspects of software development, there are no exact measures. Suggestions have been made that each statement from the detailed design notation should translate into some given number or fewer statements in the coding language. One expert recommends that the translation be ten or fewer lines of source code.[31]

Software critical design review

Once the detailed design of a software system has been completed, the system can be coded. Before coding begins, however, it is extremely important that the total system design down to each low-level component be reviewed. This final software design review is frequently called the Software Critical Design Review. Participants should include key representatives from the analysts, the system designers, the database designers, the programmers, and the system testers. Customers are also often represented at this review. See *Design to Reduce Technical Risk* for details.

The completion of the system design establishes a major milestone in a software system development process. When the design is accepted, resource estimates and allocations are updated, code and test commitments are made, schedules are confirmed, and funding sign-offs occur.

Step 5: Implement the Software System

Software implementation transforms the detailed design specifications for a system into the source code of an actual program. Development of the code is the responsibility of the programming group. A critical goal of this activity should be to develop code that is easy to read and understand, and is therefore easy to debug, test, and maintain. See Figure 12.

Information required before the start of the software implementation phase includes: the system's software requirements, the architecture documents, the functional design specifications, and the detailed design specifications. Coding objectives, such as minimizing the number of lines of code or minimizing the use of primary memory, may also be provided.

Structured programming

Structured programming or structured coding is an established technique for helping to resolve the potential problem of complex, unreadable code. A structured computer program is written so that the result can be read like a book from start to finish without flipping pages back and forth. The general rule for a programmer attempting to write structured code is to develop each routine so there is only one entry into

---

[31]Fairley, 182.

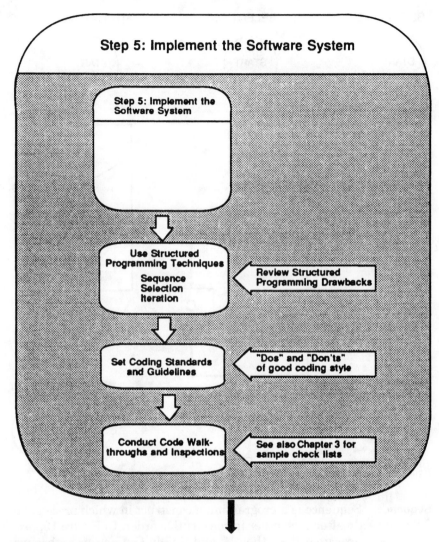

Figure 12   Implementing the software system.

it and one exit out. Excessive and undisciplined use of the "GOTO" command, if it exists, is usually prohibited.

Experts have demonstrated that only three different programming constructs are necessary to write any single-entry/single-exit routine. The three constructs, illustrated in Figure 13, are: *sequence, selection,* and *iteration*. In the figure, a box represents a procedure, function, or statement; a diamond-shaped symbol represents a decision point; and an arrow indicates control flow.

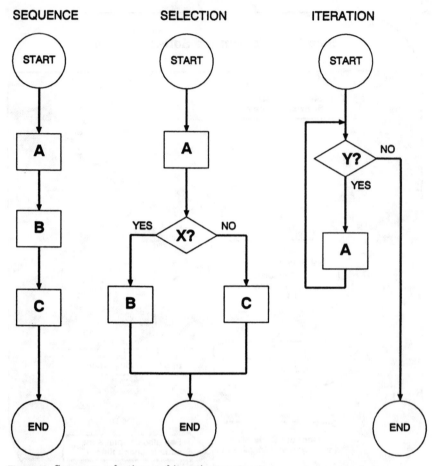

Figure 13 Sequence, selection, and iteration constructs.

Sequence.   Sequence is a programming construct in which procedures follow directly after each other in consecutive order. In Figure 13, procedure A is executed first, then B, and finally C. Each pass through that construct always follows the exact same set of procedures.

Selection.   Selection is a programming construct in which some decision must be made to determine the path to follow. The example in Figure 13 shows procedure A being executed first, then a question represented by X. If the answer to the question is "yes," procedure B is executed; if the answer to the question is "no," procedure C is executed.

Iteration.   The third programming construct, iteration, is one in which, based upon some decision point, a procedure may be repeatedly executed.

Figure 13 shows a question, X, which if answered "yes" causes procedure A to be executed and then the question is asked again. Procedure A is executed again and again until the answer to question X is "no."

Structured programming drawbacks. There is some criticism of the inefficiencies caused by strict adherence to structured programming techniques. Most analysts believe, however, that if the general principles are followed, with exceptions allowed for critical portions of a system, then the readability and maintenance of source code can be improved.

Coding standards and guidelines

Most development organizations have their own set of implementation standards and guidelines to help ensure similarity of coding and documentation formats. These standards usually pertain to a particular programming language but may also contain general rules for good programming. Fairley offers a set of eight "Dos" and eight "Don'ts" of good coding style.[32] They are:

- DO
  Use a few standard, agreed-upon control constructs
  Use GOTOs in a disciplined way
  Introduce user-defined data types to model entities in the problem domain
  Hide data structures behind access functions
  Isolate machine dependencies in a few routines
  Provide standard documentation prologues for each subprogram and/or compilation unit
  Carefully examine routines having fewer than 5 or more than 25 executable statements
  Use indentation, parentheses, blank spaces, blank lines, and borders around comment blocks to enhance readability

- DON'T
  Don't be too clever
  Don't use null THEN statements
  Don't use THEN_IF statements
  Don't nest too deeply
  Don't rely on obscure side effects
  Don't sub-optimize
  Don't pass more than five formal parameters to subroutines
  Don't use one identifier for multiple purposes

---

[32]Fairley, 210, 215.

Code walkthroughs and inspections

Code walkthroughs and inspections should be a routine practice in every software development organization. Consider the project being developed to determine which reviews are required. In some cases, every piece of code may need to be examined; in others, only critical components require inspection. During a walkthrough, the programmer leads other team members through a module of code or part of the design while they attempt to discover faults by questioning. Sample code review and code inspection checklists are provided in Chapter 3: Application. As a best practice, thorough code inspections are strongly recommended. See *Design to Reduce Technical Risk* for details.

Step 6: Test the Software

The testing phase of software development is when individual components of the software are tested and combined to verify that the software system meets the documented requirements and adheres to the predefined design. See Figure 14.

Independent testing organization

Most software experts recommend that an independent organization test a software system. One option is to contract with an outside organization for the testing. If this is not possible, the testing organization should be managerially separate from the design and development groups assigned to the project.

This recommendation is based more on observations of human nature than on substantiated fact. Effective testing groups need to have somewhat of a "destructive" view of a system, so that they can flush out errors and "break" the system. The design and development groups who have built the software system have a "constructive" view, and may therefore find it too difficult to develop the frame of mind required for testing.

Plan for software testing

A critical concept that experts strongly stress is the importance of planning and documenting software test activities *before they begin*. Whereas software testing begins after the coding phase, the plans for what to test and how to test must begin in the early stages of software development.

The Institute of Electrical and Electronics Engineers (IEEE) standards on software development require that *Software Verification and Validation Plans* be developed and documented for all software pro-

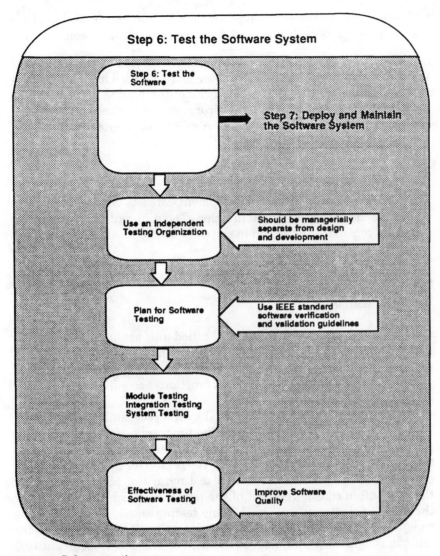

Figure 14 Software testing.

jects.[33] In the standard, the terms verification and validation are defined as follows:

- *Software verification*—determines whether or not the products of a given phase of the software development cycle fulfill the requirements established during the previous phase.

---

[33]IEEE Computer Society. 1986. *IEEE Standard for Software Verification and Validation Plans Std. 1012-1986.* IEEE, Inc. New York. 9–10.

■ *Software validation*—evaluates software at the end of the software development process to ensure compliance with software requirements.

As software development progresses, the *Software Verification and Validation Plan* (SVVP) should become more detailed until a final version is published. The plan must include: the testing objectives, the scope of the testing, the testing environment, acceptance criteria, and any constraints to the testing. The Application chapter includes the IEEE standard for software verification and validation.

Types of software testing

The testing step of software development consists of several distinct phases, each serving a unique function. The different types of testing generally considered essential in software development are

■ module (or unit) testing

■ integration testing

■ system testing

Module testing.   Module testing (also called *unit* or *component testing*) is the testing of one individual component (that is, one program module, one functional unit, or one subroutine). The objective of module testing is to determine if the module functions according to its specifications.

Module testing is usually conducted by the programmer of the module being tested. It is closely tied to the programmer's development of the code and often becomes an iterative process of testing a component, finding a problem, debugging (finding the reason for the problem in the code), fixing the problem, and then testing again. Module testing is therefore often considered part of the implementation (Step 5) rather than part of the testing phase. Module testing should nevertheless be recognized as a separate function, and should be disciplined. The tester must develop a test plan for the component and must document test cases and procedures. Too often, this discipline is overlooked and testing of individual components becomes "ad hoc" testing with no records about the actual cases, the procedures, or the results.

White box testing is frequently used during module testing. White box testing means that the tester is familiar with the internal logic of the component and develops test cases accordingly.

Code coverage (how much of the code is covered by the testing) and logic path coverage (how many of the logical paths in the code are tested) are two primary considerations when developing test cases for module testing.

Special testing procedures and tools often need to be developed to isolate modules for testing. Many programming organizations keep a library of tools (such as stub and driver routines) which can be borrowed. Other groups develop their own modules as needed. In any case, before module testing begins special procedures must be designed and documented as part of the test plan for each component.

Integration testing

After module testing, the next step in the software testing phase is integration testing. This activity involves combining components in an orderly progression until the entire system has been built. The emphasis of integration testing is on the interaction of the different components and the interfaces between them.

Most often, the programming group performs software integration testing. As with module testing, integration testing is very closely linked to the programming activity since the tester needs to know details of the function of each component to develop a good integration test plan.

Integration test techniques.   An important decision when planning for integration testing is determining the procedure to be used for combining all the individual modules. There are two basic approaches for doing this: non-incremental testing and incremental testing.

In *non-incremental integration testing,* all the software components (assuming they have each been individually module tested) are combined at once and then testing begins. Myers calls this "big bang" testing.[34] Most experts, Myers included, do not recommend this approach to integration testing because problem isolation is very difficult. Since all modules are combined at once, a failure could be in any one of the numerous interfaces that have been introduced.

The recommended approach for the integration of system components is planned *incremental testing.* With this method, one component is completely module tested and debugged. Another component is then added to the first and the combination is tested and debugged. This pattern of adding one new component at a time is repeated until all components have been added to the test and the system is completely integrated.

Incremental testing requires another decision about the order in which the components will be added to the test. There are no clear-cut rules for doing this. Testers must base a decision on their knowledge of what makes the most sense for their system, considering logic and use of resources. There are, however, two basic strategies: top-down or bottom-up.

---

[34]Myers, Glenford J. 1979. *The Art of Software Testing.* New York: John Wiley and Sons. 89.

The structure of many software systems can be defined as a hierarchy of modules with a single starting point, and with several logical paths available to traverse to the bottom of the hierarchy. Figure 15 shows a structural representation of a small system that contains eight modules: A, B, C, D, E, F, G, and H.

A tester using *top-down integration testing* on this system begins by module testing and debugging the A component. The next step is to add a new component to the test. In this case, either B or C is added. If B was chosen and tested, either C or D could be the next choice. Some testers prefer to follow one path to completion, while others prefer to complete all the modules on the same level before proceeding to a lower level of the hierarchy.

Bottom-up integration testing reverses top-down testing. With this approach, a tester simply starts at the bottom-most level of the hierarchy and works up. As shown in Figure 15, a tester might start by module testing component G. With bottom-up testing, all the components at the bottom of the hierarchy are usually module tested first and then testing proceeds in turn to each of their calling components. The primary rule in bottom-up testing is that a component should not be chosen to be the next one added to the test unless all of the components that it calls have already been tested.

System testing. The end of integration testing is usually a major milestone in the development process. It is at this point that most develop-

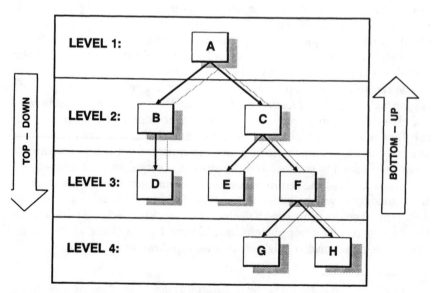

Figure 15 Structural representation of a software system.

ment organizations relinquish the code as an entire system to the appropriate organization for system testing.

System test is considered the most difficult type of testing. With the move to system test, there is also a move from structural testing to functional testing. Now, rather than testing the internal logic of the software, the tester concentrates on what the program is supposed to do and how well it does it.

The definition for system test used in the IEEE software testing standards is "the process of testing an integrated hardware and software system to verify that the system meets its specified requirements."[35] The hardware aspect of this definition is important. Frequently, module and integration tests are conducted within a development environment. Ideally, in system test, the software is tested on the actual target hardware for a system. In many cases, however, the target hardware is being built in parallel with the software and system testing may need to be conducted on prototype hardware or with a simulator.

The responsibility for software system test belongs to the group designated as the test organization, ideally independent from the software designers and programmers. System testers should be involved with a project from the beginning and should have access to the most up-to-date documentation of the system objectives, the software requirements and specifications, the architecture, the development and design methodologies used during implementation, and a complete set of the user documentation.

When the system is delivered to the testers from the development organization, a system test plan, already reviewed and accepted, should be ready for execution. Similar to the plans in the earlier testing activities, the software system test plan should be complete with scheduling, resource estimates, test cases, procedures, and acceptance criteria. Since this is generally the last step in the development life cycle before the software is passed to the customers, it is extremely important that a system test plan cover all aspects of the software and its operation.

System testing techniques. System testing is often referred to as "testing the whole system." Translated literally, that could mean that every input or output condition in the software needs to be tested for every possible logical path through the code. Even in a small system this task could become quite lengthy. In a large, complex system, it would be prohibitively time-consuming and expensive.

The system test organization must develop a strategy for testing a particular system and determine the amount of test coverage required.

---

[35] *IEEE Standard for Software Verification and Validation Plans Std. 1012-1986.* 11.

There is no cookbook for doing so. In a small noncritical system, a very low degree of test coverage may be acceptable. High coverage is needed in a critical software system involving human life. The testers must decide the best plan based on system characteristics, the environment in which the software system will operate, and the testers' experience.

In general, software system testing is done using *black box testing*. The tester, viewing the system as a black box, is not concerned with the internals, but rather is interested in finding if and when the system does not behave according to its requirements.

One technique often used for identifying specific test cases is called *equivalence partitioning*. In this method, an equivalence class is identified so that one test case covers a number of other possible test cases.

Boundary analysis is another technique used in which testing is performed on all the boundary conditions. This method tests the upper and lower boundaries of the program. In addition, it is usually wise to test around the boundaries.

A third technique that should always be applied to the testing of a program is called *error guessing*. With this method, testers use their intuition and experience to develop test cases. A good system tester is usually very effective at doing this.

The following example shows how test cases might be developed using these three techniques.

The program

For this example, consider a program into which the input can only be a whole number (X) between 10 and 100 inclusive. To test all valid inputs to this program, a system tester must test every single whole number between 10 and 100 inclusive or 91 separate test cases. Testing all invalid inputs would be impossible since the number of whole numbers less than 10 and greater than 100 is infinite.

Equivalence partitioning

To solve this testing problem, a system tester could first use equivalence partitioning to create several equivalence classes of test cases. Each equivalence class in this instance is developed to represent many possible inputs, either valid or invalid. By testing a few of the options in the equivalence class, the whole equivalence class is considered tested. Three possible equivalence classes are listed below:

- All whole numbers greater than 100 (Try $X = 254$, $X = 1000$)
- All whole numbers less than 10 (Try $X = 1$, $X = 5$)
- All whole numbers between 10 and 100 (Try $X = 47$, $X = 85$)

Boundary analysis

The three equivalence classes listed above, however, do not completely test the input conditions of the given program. Test cases need to be developed to test what happens when a user enters either the number 10 or the number 100. Since these are the boundaries of the valid input group, this technique is called boundary analysis.

Testing around the boundaries

Several more test cases that might then be added to test around the boundaries are:
$X = 9, X = 11, X = 99, X = 101.$

Error guessing

Lastly, a system tester should apply the error guessing technique to develop additional test cases. For the sample program, an experienced tester may choose the following test cases:

- a negative number
- zero
- a decimal number ($X = 15.3$)
- a non-numeric
- a blank

Other test case development techniques exist besides the ones mentioned above and there are numerous automated testing tools available today that address specific testing problems. System testers should explore the tools available for their particular testing environment.

Regression testing. Regression Testing is retesting software that has been modified in order to ensure that new errors have not been introduced into the system. Software maintenance involves changing programs as a result of errors found or a modification in user requirements. Such changes are liable to introduce new errors into the software. There are a variety of static analysis and dynamic testing techniques for performing regression tests as well as several regression testing tools. Regression testing should be an integral part of the test plan and software test activities.

System test categories. Reiterating that system testing is the process of ensuring that the system does what it is supposed to do, Myers has identified 15 different categories for which test cases need to be developed for effective system testing.[36]

Facility Testing. Ensuring that the program performs each function specified in the objectives. This type of testing is at a very high level and does not measure how well or how effectively the program does what it is expected to do.

Volume Testing. Testing with a heavy volume of data. For example, if a database program is expected to accept an input file of data values, volume testing might mean creating an extremely large number of data values to be entered at one time. Often this type of testing finds failures with declared buffer sizes or input arrays.

---

[36]Myers, *The Art of Software Testing,* 110–118.

Stress Testing. Testing a system under heavy load conditions. If an objective of the system is to support 20 simultaneous users with a given response rate, stress testing may begin with 20 users and continue to add additional users until response rates noticeably decrease. For this type of testing, a system test group often develops test simulators. Simulators are generally software programs or hardware devices that can be tuned to simulate various levels of stress conditions. In this case, the simulator appears as if 20 or more users were on the system when there may be only one system tester.

Usability Testing. Testing the human or user interface of the system. Many development organizations today use human factors engineers to analyze the user aspects of a system, including making sure error messages are meaningful, the system is easy to use, and the number of keystrokes required is not excessive.

Security Testing. Testing a system to determine if it inadvertently allows unauthorized entry into the system or unauthorized access to sensitive data. System security is extremely important in most government projects and for many systems in the business world.

Performance Testing. Testing a system against the objectives that have been specified regarding response time, throughput rates, start-up times, and capacity. Performance standards in operating systems, database management systems, communications software, and real-time applications are critical to success.

Storage Testing. Testing the system to reveal problems related to the requirements for amounts of storage used by the program, the size of the system, or the size of the files the program uses.

Configuration Testing. Testing the system to determine if it supports the various hardware and communications configurations for which it was designed. In particular, many systems have a base set of required components and a set of optional components. Each combination should be tested.

Compatibility Testing. Testing to ascertain whether the system meets objectives concerning compatibility with other systems.

Conversion Testing. Testing objectives for converting from a former system to the new system. This is an important concern when the old system must remain operational during the conversion or when large amounts of data need to be converted.

Installability Testing. Testing to uncover problems in the installation procedures for the system.

Reliability Testing. Testing against specific objectives that detail how reliable a system is expected to be. Examples of reliability objectives are: Mean Time To Failure (MTTF), Mean Time Between Failures (MTBF), maximum number of errors detected after deployment, and percent of downtime.

Recovery Testing. Testing to ensure that a system can recover from its own failures or failures by related hardware, software, and communications failures. Recovery requirements are very common in operating systems and in critical applications systems.

Serviceability Testing. Testing the objectives that have been specified for maintaining and operating the system. Auxiliary programs such as audit routines and diagnostic routines are examples of programs that need to be tested for serviceability.

Documentation Testing. Testing the documentation that will be delivered to the user with the system. This includes end-user manuals as well as operations and maintenance documentation.

Procedure Testing. Testing the human procedures associated with the system. Examples include database administration procedures and system back-up procedures.

Quality, cost, and time are the three customer concerns when contracting for a software system. If system testing is well-planned and executed, errors are uncovered that would eventually have been found by customers and would conceivably have caused severe impact on their operations. System testing, therefore, is a major contributor to the delivery of a more reliable system within the scheduled timeframe and within budget.

Effectiveness of software testing

Musa, Iannino, and Okumoto collected data about the number of faults found in software during the various stages of development and estimated the mean fault density remaining at the beginning of each development phase. Their data strongly supports software testing as an effective means for significantly improving the quality of a software system.

Figure 16 shows the data from the Musa, Iannino and Okumoto study. According to their estimates, a software product in the coding stage, after compilation and assembly, has a mean fault density of 99.5 faults per 1,000 source lines. Their next estimates show by the beginning of module test, the number of faults per 1,000 source lines has been reduced to 19.7. This dramatic reduction is attributed to desk checking and code inspections. Module testing and integration testing cause another big drop in the number of faults so that as the software enters system test, the mean fault density is estimated to be 6.01 faults per 1,000 source lines. Finally, by the beginning of system operation, the estimated fault density is only 1.48 faults per 1,000 source lines.[37]

---

[37]Musa, John D., Anthony Iannino, and Kazuhiro Okumoto. 1987. *Software Reliability: Measurement, Prediction, Application.* New York: McGraw-Hill. 118.

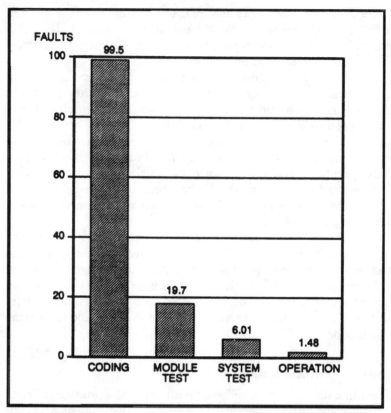

Figure 16 Faults per 1,000 source lines (found on entering the indicated phase).

Step 7: Deploy and Maintain the Software System

When a software organization has completed all the development and testing of a system, it continues to the next phase, deployment. This may include installation, acceptance test, operation, and maintenance of the software system.

Software deployment activities vary substantially depending on the type of system being installed and the particular circumstances related to that system. For instance, the system may be

- a replacement for an older system, thus requiring system conversion to phase out the old
- a completely new system being installed for the first time
- an upgrade of a real-time system requiring uninterrupted service during the deployment

- part of a complex hardware and software system requiring considerable coordination activities

An overview of the process is shown in Figure 17.

Software installation and conversion

The initial installation of any new or replacement software system is usually done via a beta test. If the completed system will eventually be installed at numerous user sites, one of these sites is chosen as the beta test site. During the beta test period, the new system is installed on the target hardware, and system conversion activities, if required, are completed. Users then begin to use the new system. Before any software system is installed, however, the development organization should prepare a complete system installation plan and review it with the customers, the user organization, and the system operations group.

During the initial installation or the early use of a software system at a user's site, errors often surface due to unexpected aspects of the user's environment. A system failure during this time could cause serious setbacks for users, especially on critical real-time systems. Because of this, the system installation plan should cover the installation, conversion, and beta test periods, and should include prearranged agreements about

- installation and conversion schedules
- resources required
- error repair timeframes
- system contingencies and plans
- system recovery
- training

Acceptance test

The customers, the users, and the development organization should also agree about a time during the beta test period when the software will be baselined and a formal customer test of the software, called an *acceptance test,* will begin. As with all other tests of the system, the acceptance test must be a planned activity that includes a test plan, test procedures, test cases, and the acceptance criteria.

During acceptance test, the system's users should attempt to perform every system activity. User training before the acceptance test is a critical success factor for a software system, as are the quality and the accuracy of the user documentation.

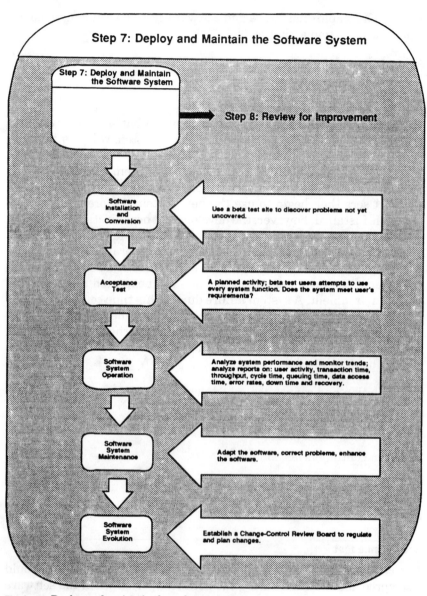

Figure 17 Deploy and maintain the software system.

When the acceptance test is complete, there should be documented data about whether the system meets the customer's requirements. If the system is accepted, it officially enters the operation and maintenance phase of its life cycle. If there are multiple target user sites for this system, a schedule should be developed for deployment at those sites.

If the software system is not acceptable, the customer and the developers should agree on what changes are necessary for the system to meet the objectives. They should also agree on the proposed schedule and procedures for delivering the revised system. In some cases, an unacceptable system remains in operation at a customer's site and revisions are added to the system and tested as they become available. If the new system is a replacement system, a customer may request that the old system be reinstalled until the new system can be revised to meet stated objectives.

Software system operation

The operation of a software system is the ongoing process of running the system. Some software systems are required to run 24 hours a day, 7 days a week; some have Mean Time Between Failure (MTBF) requirements that cannot be exceeded; and others may have specific performance tolerances within which the system must conform. As with every other phase of a software system, the operation phase should be planned and documented. Procedures for managing the operation, for evaluating the operation, and for providing information about operational problems are required.

System performance reports should be periodically scheduled and analyzed to ensure proper system operation and to monitor operational trends in the system's performance. Common software operational reports include statistics about the following aspects of the system:

- user activity
- transaction time
- throughput rate
- cycle time
- queuing time
- system access time
- data access time
- error rates

Software system maintenance

The maintenance period of a software system covers customer acceptance of the initial system to system retirement. The primary activities included in the maintenance period are: correcting software problems, developing system enhancements, and adapting the system to a new environment. Figure 18 illustrates the typical distribution of these

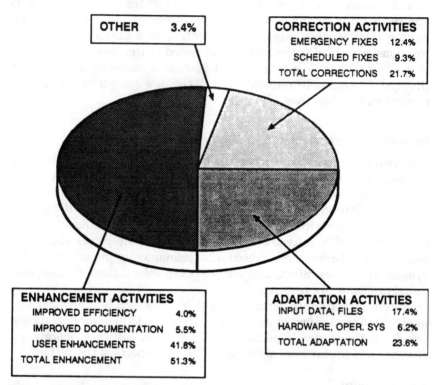

MAINTENANCE EFFORT DISTRIBUTION

OTHER   3.4%

CORRECTION ACTIVITIES
EMERGENCY FIXES   12.4%
SCHEDULED FIXES   9.3%
TOTAL CORRECTIONS   21.7%

ENHANCEMENT ACTIVITIES
IMPROVED EFFICIENCY   4.0%
IMPROVED DOCUMENTATION   5.5%
USER ENHANCEMENTS   41.8%
TOTAL ENHANCEMENT   51.3%

ADAPTATION ACTIVITIES
INPUT DATA, FILES   17.4%
HARDWARE, OPER. SYS   6.2%
TOTAL ADAPTATION   23.6%

Figure 18 Distribution of maintenance efforts.

maintenance activities, determined from a survey of 487 business data processing installations.[38]

In some cases, the maintenance period of a software system may be as long as 10 to 15 years and may account for as much as 70 percent of the total system costs. This means software maintenance should be planned early in the development life cycle, and maintainability should be a design and implementation consideration.

Enhancing software maintainability. Key development activities that can enhance the maintainability of a software system include:

- standardization of design notations for data flows, structures, algorithms, interface specifications, pseudocode, and data dictionaries

---

[38]Fairley, 83.

- emphasis on clarity of code and modularization through the use of information hiding, data abstraction, and single-entry and single-exit constructs
- coding style standards including program prologues, comment lines, indentation, parameters, and error handling
- guidelines and requirements for supporting documentation such as a user manual, a maintenance guide, an error message manual, test documentation, and cross-reference directories
- keeping all documents up-to-date

Configuration management during maintenance. During the maintenance phase of a software system, it is very important to use a configuration management system to track and control both the software and the documentation of the system. A description of change control and configuration management is described in Step 2 of this chapter. Important features of a configuration system during software maintenance include a history of component revisions, version control by site, an accounting of the number of errors reported, fixed and released to the field, and documentation updates.

Software system evolution

Over time, enhancements and adaptations may cause substantial cumulative changes in a software system. These changes often increase the size and complexity of a system while decreasing its flexibility. When this happens, the maintenance of the software system can become difficult and even small fixes or enhancements become costly. Often, a minor problem results in a major system failure.

Change Control Review Board. To help avoid these problems, system changes should be carefully regulated. Many software organizations use a Change Control Review Board to consider and approve all changes. The membership of this board (and the rules by which it operates) vary depending on the nature of the software. The two primary objectives of the board are to review all change requests and establish priorities and constraints for making changes. In some cases, however, a software system simply outgrows its originally planned and designed bounds. It then becomes more cost-effective to replace the entire system than to continue to patch the old one.

Step 8: Review for Improvement

The goal for software projects, like other development projects, is continual improvement in quality or productivity. This goal is typically achieved little by little rather than with major bursts. These incremental improvements, however, can add up to large differences in the software system over the course of time. In quality, the improvements come from reducing errors, finding errors early, and meeting requirements for function and usage. In productivity, improvements come from meeting customer needs while avoiding waste from redesign, repair, or maintenance.

Sustained high quality and productivity require a disciplined application of process improvement. To do this, software development organizations must allocate resources to review the outcome of each of their projects and the processes under which each project was developed. (See Step 2 for suggested outcome and process metrics.)

Figure 19 shows an overview of the improvement process.

Software development postmortems

A *postmortem* provides an excellent way for a software organization to evaluate its development process. A postmortem is an assessment done after the completion of a project or major development phase, when team members can look at the processes objectively.

A postmortem identifies successes so that they can be maintained. Data gathered from the postmortem can also be used for planning future projects and for identifying specific areas for quality improvement within the organization. Since the key focus of a postmortem is generally the *process* under which the software was developed, it can almost be considered a debriefing of the project members.

Customers and users may also be interviewed during a project's postmortem. They frequently provide valuable information and insight into the project's development processes.

During a postmortem, risk areas are studied. Items of technical risk are listed and prioritized; attendees offer ways of managing the risk. In this way, the cost of doing postmortems is justified since improving the process will reduce costs in the long run.

Examples of postmortem topics. Examples of topics explored during postmortems include:

- the management techniques used on the project
- the assignment of project responsibilities
- the development methodology chosen
- the project's standards (for example, documentation and change control) and how well standards were followed
- the amount of project-specific and technological experience on the team

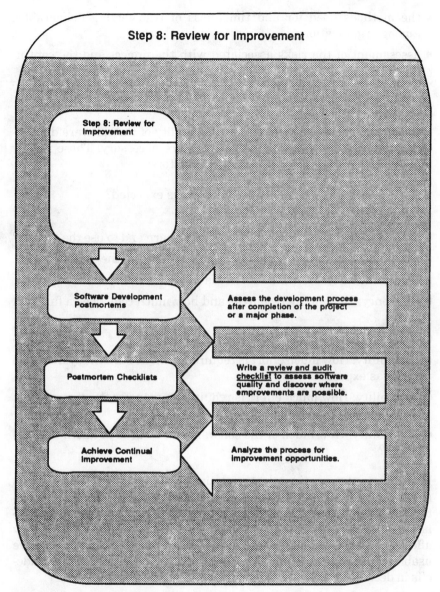

Figure 19 Review for improvement.

- the level of training provided to team members
- the tools and technologies used
- the degree of communication between management and the team, between the various organizations involved with the project, among the team members, and between the development team and the customer

- the methods used for and timeliness of transferring deliverables among organizations
- assessment of the risks associated with the project and the contingency plans

Postmortem checklists

Postmortem checklists help assess the quality of the software deliverables and discover where improvements are necessary. These review and audit checklists often include these factors:

- Correctness: Does the software perform as expected?
- Reliability: How accurate is it?
- Usability: How much effort does it take to learn and to use the system?
- Flexibility: How much effort is required to modify the system?
- Maintainability: How much effort is required to find and fix errors?
- Efficiency: How many resources and how much code does a function take?
- Integrity: Is unauthorized access controlled?
- Testability: How much effort is required to make sure the system performs as expected?
- Portability: How much effort is required to transfer the system from one machine or environment to another?
- Reusability: How much of the software can be used in another application?

It is important to consider the correlations between factors. Correlations may be positive in that improving one factor also improves another factor; for example, improving reliability also improves correctness. Correlations may be negative in that improvements in one factor negatively affect another, for example, the added code and processing to improve usability may make the program less efficient. Thus, consider the trade-offs in deciding which improvements to pursue.

Achieving continual improvements

Continuous process improvement is iterative. Process analysis involves deciding which improvements to pursue, implementing the improvements, checking and assessing the results, and then planning the next improvements. The efforts pay off, however, in improved customer satisfaction, increased productivity, and lower costs.

3

Application

This chapter provides five specific examples of applications for the procedures in Chapter 2.

- Concept definition is illustrated by a sample Software Feasibility Report. It is meant to be a suggested framework for guiding feasibility studies.

- Project planning is often considered to be the most difficult segment of software development, and its greatest challenge lies in correct estimation of cost, staff, and time. The COCOMO model for effort and cost estimation is one way to meet this challenge, and its methodology is shown as an example.

- The IEEE Standard for a Software Verification and Validation Plan is presented as a framework, to be customized for every project.

- The heart of any software project is, of course, its code. The code inspection example describes items of concern during a code review. The list of items, while extensive, should be considered only as a jumping-off point for actual reviews.

- Two Software System Test Plans are presented, an example of a good plan and an example of one that needs more work.

Software Feasibility Report

The first step in a software engineering project is to define the concept. This chapter presents a practical application of the concept definition stage: a sample of a Software Feasibility Report.

The flow of ideas

Ideas for new products can come from several sources: the research lab, marketing department, or the proposal development organization, to name a few. From there, a formal selection process should be encouraged, with research into alternatives. Those selected should be subject to a formal feasibility study, with the result being a feasibility report. Figure 20[39] shows the four major analyses: customer needs, competitive, functional, and economic.

Target of the software feasibility report

The outcome of the concept definition stage should be a formal software feasibility report targeted for management, users, and developers.[40]

This high-level document must be a clear, concise statement of user needs and technical risks, and a description of how the proposed system will or will not meet those needs and handle the risks. Indeed, the feasibility study will be reviewed with the users, and it should be written in user terminology that is easily understood.

In addition to a general description of the proposed system in its "finished" state, the report should contain preliminary estimates for development cost, staff, and time. Management's go/no go decision should be based on the contents of this report; the importance of their approval is signified by making this a "sign-off document."

Framework for the report

There are many factors involved in the consideration of feasibility, and the report must address the ones that are important to the company and the project. Software development organizations should develop their own standard feasibility report framework based on items identified as significant. A sample framework begins on page 194. Remember, it is just a sample; you must customize it to your needs.

---

[39]Starr, Martin K. 1988. *Operations Management*. Englewood Cliffs, NJ: Prentice-Hall. 88.

[40]Kirk, Frank. *Total System Development for Information Systems*, 57–63.

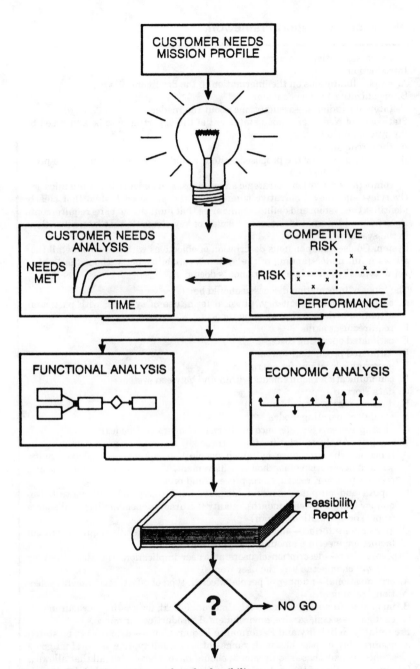

Figure 20 Evaluating a new product for feasibility.

Sample Feasibility Report Framework

1. Abstract—executive summary
2. Introduction
   A. scope—limitations on the information in the document
   B. organization of the document
   C. intended audience—assumptions about the reader
3. Statement of Need—expanded statement of the opportunity to be addressed by the system, including:
   A. the circumstances
   B. description of how the proposed system would correct or eliminate the problem or fulfill the need
   C. competitive situations, strategic advantages, and benefits to the organization
4. Overview—high-level narrative summary of the proposed system that clearly identifies the system and defines boundaries that limit the set of its requirements
5. External and Internal Interfaces—display of key elements that interact with or in the system
6. System Goals—unambiguous description of objectives with a level of detail that allows a full understanding of the system's capability but without the level of detail typically found in a requirements document

   The types of information discussed should be
   A. output—content, frequency, physical form, use of symbols; with particular attention to data and processing reports
   B. required user skills
   C. estimated operating costs
   D. estimated production volume
   E. geographic locations for operation
   F. communication requirements within and between systems
   G. data storage
   H. data security
   I. available operating modes
   J. backup systems (or reference to alternative operating modes)
7. Capabilities Analysis—clarification of three key factors for each capability:
   A. function—the procedure by which people and equipment produce results, without description of method of achievement. The six primary functions are: receive, transfer, record, store, process, and present.
   B. inputs and outputs—medium (display, hard copy), volume/quantity, frequency (per day, week, month), quality (accuracy, dependability), and source (input) or destination (output)
   C. personnel interface—number of people and types of skills required, human factors engineering, amount and type of training
8. Expected Users—description of users and user implications (i.e., how the new system will change the way the user works)
   A. organizational—number of people affected, type of effect, recruitment, selection, training
   B. business—financial, managerial, time, analytical, forecasting, measurement
   C. customer—social, service, environmental, product performance
9. Preliminary Reliability and Performance Requirements—strictures to be stated as quantifiably as possible, with ranges of acceptability; like the system goals (described above), these requirements should have a level of detail that allows a full understanding of the system's capability but without the level of detail typically found in a requirements document
   A. response time—definition (expressed in terms of access time) and projections of duration from input to output

    B accuracy—definition and frequency of significant errors

    C. availability of total system—including frequency and duration of degraded performance modes

    D. flexibility—type and number of exceptional conditions handled by the system

    E. security—including legal safety and degree of vulnerability

    F. capacity—average and peak loads

    G. customer acceptance—by management and by user

    H. efficiency or productivity—performance ratio

    I. quality—tolerance and appearance

10. Assumptions, Items for Resolution—any items discovered while doing the study, stated with best- and worst-case scenarios

11. Resources and Constraints—factors already in existence and/or for which there is planned expansion

    A. physical plant facilities, supplies

    B. hardware, software, and firmware technology

    C. development staff, time, and budget

    D. current and potential system interfaces

    E. environmental conditions such as company organization, union contracts, laws, regulations

    F. consonance with short- and long-range company goals

        Each resource should be examined for development and for the finished product and should be listed together with its

        A. best- and worst-case analyses

        B. degree of confidence of the analyses

        C. identification of the criticality of resources and constraints; if very critical, the ease of changing the restriction

12. Possible System Configurations—these should describe functionality only (without reference to particular hardware); e.g., several terminal communications media, a central processing unit, some off-line storage

13. Impact and Cost Analysis—estimates for the cost of development (personnel, facilities), operation, maintenance, and support; forecast of demand or usage and expected revenues; other impacts on the state of the art in weapons systems (or other government activities); impact on the overall DoD procurement effort. Describe the estimates, forecasts, and impacts

    A. for all the possible system configurations

    B. with identification of possible savings and/or additional costs

    C. with numbers expressed as high-low ranges, stated together with a probable figure

14. Estimate of Development Schedule—high-level display of time vs. staff, coordinated by life cycle phase, including interactions with users and other involved groups, and taking into account the following items:

    A. communications

    B. budget

    C work space

    D. job aids

    E. special equipment

    F. staff requirements (number of, skills, knowledge)

    G. development objectives

    H. scheduling network

    I. activity time status reports

    J. function bar charts

    K. cost milestone reports

(Continued)

Sample Feasibility Report Framework (Continued)

L. staff loading
M. financial plans
N. status reports

15. Ranked Control Objectives—preliminary proposed orders based on importance to the user and on economic, technological, and operational feasibility. Although they will be stated here in high-level terms, these goals may be expected to remain constant and not be significantly altered in any forthcoming requirements document.
   A. system administration
   B. data storage and security
   C. error detection
   D. regulatory and company policy requirements
   E. audit trail
   F. system reliability
   G. system maintainability

16. Customer Acceptance Criteria—the features and timing that prospective customers are willing and committed to accept and on which they will base their "go" or "no-go" decisions

17. Management Acceptance Criteria—high-level discussion of the basis for "go" or "no-go" on the project

18. Risk Assessment—high-level discussion of "what-ifs" and key issues of concern as well as the likelihood of the realization of these concerns

19. Recommended Action—"go" or "no-go" and the elements that are paramount to the recommendation

Appendix I   Terminology—project-specific terms, acronyms, conventions, and language standards

Appendix II   Methodology of the Study—ongoing research; interviews with users, developers, subject matter experts; literature search; type of cost analysis; analysis of current and projected staffing levels, funding levels, physical plant; market research and analysis

Appendix III References—a brief list of references used during the study; not an exhaustive historical survey

Effort and Cost Estimation

An important activity in planning a software project is predicting the resources that are needed for the project and the costs that will be incurred during its life cycle. Several different types of software costing methods were discussed in Chapter 2: Procedures: expert estimation, project similarity, lines of code estimation, and cost estimation modeling.

This chapter gives an example of a software cost estimation method. The COCOMO (COnstructive COst MOdel) cost estimation method originated with Barry Boehm and is widely used, particularly in government projects. This discussion is neither an endorsement of the model nor a complete tutorial for using the model. Instead, the model is used in this chapter to highlight the issues and factors that must be considered when estimating software resources. In fact, Boehm believes that the model's biggest asset is not the methodology itself, but rather COCOMO's provision of a "common universe of discourse" for understanding software tradeoffs, for management negotiation and control, and for improving software productivity.[41]

The remainder of this chapter

- defines the COCOMO model
- describes the steps of the COCOMO Intermediate model
- applies that model to a software communication project

Although detailed, the example does not cover every aspect of the COCOMO model.

What is COCOMO?

COCOMO is a method of estimating the effort, schedule, and cost of a planned software project by analyzing the attributes of the project and applying that information to a set of standard equations. The basis for the model, its equations, and its charts is a study conducted in the late 1970s at TRW in which the estimated and actual project team member-months of 63 projects were analyzed along with data about the type of projects, the complexity, and the skill level of analysts and programmers on the projects.

As shown in Figure 21, the COCOMO model requires a cost estimator. The cost estimator is an analyst or manager familiar with cost estimation methods who determines estimates of software size, and product, computer, personnel, and project attributes. These estimates and attributes are used with various look-up tables to determine factors. The factors are used with various look-up equations to estimate costs, staffing estimates, and rough schedules. There are three different levels of COCOMO models—basic, intermediate, and detailed— each respectively building on the lower level model and providing more accurate and more detailed estimates. There are also COCOMO extensions available for various programming language development environments.

Steps in effort and cost estimation

The steps required to estimate the effort, schedule, resources, and costs of a software project differ depending on the model being used. This dis-

[41]Boehm, Barry W. 1981. *Software Engineering Economics,* 42; and Presentation, Washington, D.C., May 1989.

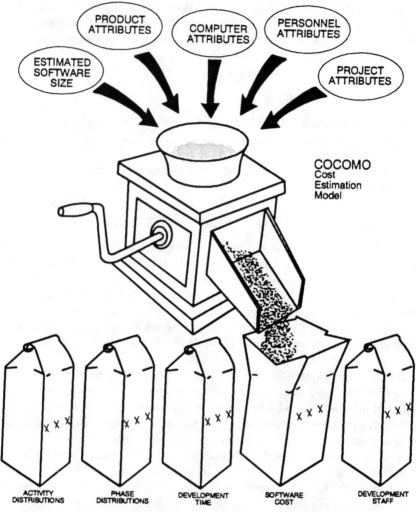

Figure 21 The COnstructive COst MOdel (COCOMO).

cussion focuses on the Intermediate COCOMO model. The steps of the Intermediate model are listed below and each is then briefly discussed:

- classify the project mode
- size the project
- determine the nominal effort
- rate the cost factors

- assign effort multipliers to the cost factors
- calculate the effort and schedule estimates
- calculate the phase distributions
- estimate the cost

Classify the project mode. First, the cost estimator must pick one of three development modes: the organic, the semidetached, or the embedded mode. This classification is important because the effort and schedule equations in the model are based on the mode chosen for the project.

The organic mode classification refers to projects that are relatively small (less than 50,000 lines of code), have little concurrent development of new hardware, and have a minimal need for innovative data processing. Examples of organic mode projects are batch data reduction, scientific models, business models, and simple inventory or production control systems.

The semidetached mode is usually chosen for medium to large projects (up to 300,000 lines of code) that have requirements for complex interfaces with hardware or other software systems. Typical semidetached systems include transaction processing systems, new operating systems, new database management systems, and simple command-control systems.

Any size project can be classified as embedded mode if it requires complex interfaces with hardware, firmware, and other software systems, extensive or innovative data processing architecture and algorithms, and if there are tight constraints on reliability and performance. Large and complex transaction processing systems, very large operating systems, ambitious command-control systems, and avionics systems are all classified as embedded mode.

Size the project. Next, the cost estimator must determine a size estimate for the project. Many of the software cost estimation models available today (including COCOMO) are based on an estimate of the number of lines of code required for a project. Sizing is not easy since there are many variables and dependencies that must be considered in the estimate. One way of guessing this number is to use PERT sizing: this requires estimation of the lowest possible size, the most likely size, and the highest possible size. These estimates are then put into various PERT formulae to give estimated total size.

Determine nominal effort. The COCOMO model next requires the cost estimator to determine the nominal effort for an average project of this size (as determined by lines of code).

Rate the cost factors.   Boehm has chosen 15 different attributes to be considered when you estimate software development efforts and costs. The attributes are:

- product attributes
  required reliability (RELY)
  database size (DATA)
  software product complexity (CPLX)
- computer attributes
  execution time constraint (TIME)
  main storage constraint (STOR)
  virtual machine volatility (VIRT)
  turnaround time constraint (TURN)
- personnel attributes
  analyst capability (ACAP)
  applications experience (AEXP)
  programmer capability (PCAP)
  virtual machine experience (VEXP)
  programming language experience (LEXP)
- project attributes
  use of modern programming practices (MODP)
  use of software tools (TOOL)
  required development schedule (SCED)

The cost estimator must examine each attribute as it relates to the given project and rate its applicability as: Very Low, Low, Nominal, High, Very High, or Extra High.

For instance, the execution time constraints (TIME) of a business data processing project may be considered average, so a cost estimator would rate the execution time constraints factor as nominal. However, a real-time software system would have tight requirements on response time and processing time and would therefore require the execution time constraints factor to be rated Very High or Extra High.

Boehm has provided some criteria that a cost estimator may use for assigning these ratings. (See Table 3.)

Assign effort multipliers to the cost factors.   In the Intermediate COCOMO model, the rating of each cost factor has associated effort multipliers. These multipliers are used to determine how the effort for this project will vary from the average project. The values for these multipliers (included in Table 4) are from the TRW study mentioned earlier.

As an example of how these effort multipliers work in the COCOMO model, consider the ACAP factor—analyst capability. If a cost estima-

TABLE 3 Software Cost Factors

Cost factor	Very low	Low	Ratings nominal	High	Very high	Extra high
			Product Attributes			
Required Reliability (RELY)	Effect: slight inconvenience	Low, easily recoverable losses	Moderate, recoverable losses	High financial loss	Risk to human life	
Database Size (DATA)		$\dfrac{\text{DB bytes}}{\text{Prog.DSI}} < 10$	$10 \le \dfrac{D}{P} < 100$	$100 \le \dfrac{D}{P} < 1000$	$\dfrac{D}{P} \ge 1000$	
Software Product Complexity (CPLX)	See Boehm, *Software Engineering Economics*, p. 122.					
			Computer Attributes			
Execution Time Constraint (TIME)			≤50% use of available execution time	70%	85%	95%
Main Storage Constraint (STOR)			≤50% use of available storage	70%	85%	95%
Virtual Machine Volatility (VIRT)		Major change every 12 months Minor: 1 month	Major: 6 months Minor: 2 weeks	Major: 2 months Minor: 1 week	Major: 2 weeks Minor: 2 days	
Turnaround Time Constraint (TURN)		Interactive	Average turnaround <4 hours	4–12 hours	>12 hours	
			Personnel Attributes			
Analyst Capability (ACAP)	15th percentile	35th percentile	55th percentile	75th percentile	90th percentile	
Applications Experience (AEXP)	≤4 months experience	1 year	3 years	6 years	12 years	
Programmer Capability (PCAP)	15th percentile	35th percentile	55th percentile	75th percentile	90th percentile	

TABLE 3 Software Cost Factors (Continued)

Cost factor	Very low	Low	Ratings nominal	High	Very high	Extra high
			Personnel Attributes (Continued)			
Virtual Machine Experience (VEXP)	≤1 month experience	4 months	1 year	3 years		
Prog. Language Experience (LEXP)	≤1 month experience	4 months	1 year	3 years		
			Project Attributes			
Modern Prog. Practices (MODP)	No use	Beginning use	Some use	General use	Routine use	
Use of Software Tools (TOOL)	Basic microprocessor tools	Basic mini tools	Basic mini/maxi tools	Strong maxi programming	Add requirements, design, management documentation tools	
Required Development Schedule (SCED)	75%	85%	100%	130%	160%	

TABLE 4 Software Development Effort Multipliers

Cost factor	Very low	Low	Ratings nominal	High	Very high	Extra high
Product Attributes						
Required Reliability (RELY)	0.75	0.88	1.00	1.15	1.40	
Database Size (DATA)		0.94	1.00	1.08	1.16	
Software Product Complexity (CPLX)	0.70	0.85	1.00	1.15	1.30	1.65
Computer Attributes						
Execution Time Constraint (TIME)			1.00	1.11	1.30	1.66
Main Storage Constraint (STOR)			1.00	1.06	1.21	1.56
Virtual Machine Volatility (VIRT)		0.87	1.00	1.15	1.30	
Turnaround Time Constraint (TURN)		0.87	1.00	1.07	1.15	
Personal Attributes						
Analyst Capability (ACAP)	1.46	1.19	1.00	0.86	0.71	
Applications Experience (AEXP)	1.29	1.13	1.00	0.91	0.82	
Programmer Capability (PCAP)	1.42	1.17	1.00	0.86	0.70	
Virtual Machine Experience (VEXP)	1.21	1.10	1.00	0.90		
Prog. Language Experience (LEXP)	1.14	1.07	1.00	0.95		
Project Attributes						
Modern Prog. Practices (MODP)	1.24	1.10	1.00	0.91	0.82	
Use of Software Tools (TOOL)	1.24	1.10	1.00	0.91	0.83	
Required Development Schedule (SCED)	1.23	1.08	1.00	1.04	1.10	

tor perceives that the analysts available for a project have average capabilities, the ACAP cost factor should be given a nominal rating. The effort multiplier associated with a nominal rating for any of the cost factors is 1.00 (see Table 4), thus ACAP is assigned a 1.00 value.

If, however, the analysts are perceived as having better than average capabilities, ACAP may be assigned a high rating. The high rating has an associated multiplier of .86. Using .86 as a multiplier for the average effort estimate for the project decreases the estimate. This is understandable since management can usually expect reduced effort and shorter schedules when there are experienced and talented resources on a project.

The reverse is also true. That is, if analysts' capabilities are perceived as less than average, management might expect longer estimates for work and possibly more rework. The problem of less than average capabilities is handled by assigning the ACAP factor a low rating and a multiplier of 1.19, with a resulting higher-than-average estimate of resources for the project.

Calculate the effort and schedule estimates. Once the size, the development mode, and the appropriate cost factor ratings and values have been identified, the next step in the Intermediate COCOMO model is to apply that information to a given set of effort and schedule equations.

The effort equations provided by Boehm give an estimate of the total development effort in team member-months (MM) required by the project. This effort estimate is then used within the scheduling equation to calculate an estimate of time, in months, required for a project. The cost estimator may then determine the number of people needed for the development phase of the project by calculations using the effort and time estimates.

The attributes of different types of software projects affect development efforts and schedules. Because of this, Boehm provides specific effort and schedule equations for each of the development modes (organic, semidetached, and embedded) in the model. The example that follows at the end of this chapter gives the equations used for an embedded mode project.

Calculate the phase distributions. For some projects, especially smaller ones, an estimate of the resources required and the duration of the development effort is enough information for further project planning. For large projects, further refinement of effort and schedule estimates may be necessary. The Intermediate COCOMO model provides a method of distributing portions of the effort and schedule estimates to each of the different phases of a software project.

TABLE 5 Phase Distribution (Effort)

Effort distribution	Project Size				
Phase	Small 2 KDSI	Intermediate 8 KDSI	Medium 32 KDSI	Large 128 KDSI	Very large 512 KDSI
Product Design	18%	18%	18%	18%	18%
Programming	60%	57%	54%	51%	48%
Integration and Test	22%	25%	28%	31%	34%

TABLE 6 Phase Distribution (Schedule)

Schedule distribution	Project size				
Phase	Small 2 KDSI	Intermediate 8 KDSI	Medium 32 KDSI	Large 128 KDSI	Very large 512 KDSI
Product Design	30%	32%	34%	36%	38%
Programming	48%	44%	40%	36%	32%
Integration and Test	22%	24%	26%	28%	30%

The COCOMO model provides tables that can be used to estimate the distribution of effort and schedule across the phases of the project. The distribution of the estimates is shown as a percentage. (See Tables 5 and 6.)[42]

Estimate the cost. A common method for estimating software development cost is first to identify the number of months of effort required for a project, then multiply by the average monthly cost.

Using the COCOMO model, a cost estimator can provide a high-level cost breakdown of a total project effort as well as costs broken down by schedule or phase.

A COCOMO example

The following is an example (adapted from Barry Boehm) of how to use the steps of the COCOMO Intermediate model to determine the effort, schedule, resources, and cost estimates for a project.[43]

---

[42]Boehm, *Software Engineering Economics,* 90.

[43]Boehm, *Software Engineering Economics,* 524–529 and Presentation.

Sample Application of COCOMO Model

Project Description

The project is a software product that will be used to process communications on a new commercial computer.

Classify the Project Mode

The development of communications software is complex because of performance constraints and because of requirements to interface with hardware, firmware, and other software in the system. Thus, the project is classified as an embedded mode development.

Size the Project

The size estimate for this project is 30 KDSI (that is, 30,000 delivered source instructions, or 30,000 lines of code).

Determine Nominal Effort

The cost estimator uses the following equation determined by Boehm from the TRW study to calculate the nominal development effort, in team member-months (MM), for embedded mode projects:

$$MM_{nom} = 2.8 \ (KDSI)^{1.20}$$

where: MM_{nom} = the team member-months of effort required for a nominal project, and

KDSI = the estimated number of delivered source instructions in thousands.

The result is a nominal effort estimate of about 165 MM for the communications software project. This is calculated by substituting 30 KDSI into the equation:

$$MM_{nom} = 2.8(30)^{1.20} = 165 \ MM$$

Note: For the COCOMO model, as well as for other cost estimation models, on-line programs for doing the necessary calculations are generally available.

Rate the Cost Factors

The next step is to examine the 15 attributes and apply a rating of Very Low, Low, Nominal, High, Very High, or Extra High.

Assign Effort Multipliers to the Cost Factors

For many projects, not all 15 cost factors used in the COCOMO model will be assigned the Nominal rating. The cost estimator for the communications project in our example decided that the factors given in the following table apply to the project. The table includes explanations for the ratings.

Cost Factors for Example Project

Cost Factor	Situation	Rating	Effort Multiplier
Required Reliability (RELY)	Local use of system. No serious recovery problems	Nominal	1.00
Database Size (DATA)	20,000 bytes	Low	0.94
Software Product Complexity (CPLX)	Communications processing	Very High	1.30
Execution Time Constraint (TIME)	Will use 70% of available time	High	1.11
Main Storage Constraint (STOR)	45K or 64K store (70%)	High	1.06
Virtual Machine Volatility (VIRT)	Based on commercial microprocessor hardware	Nominal	1.00
Turnaround Time Constraint (TURN)	Two-hour average turnaround time	Nominal	1.00
Analyst Capability (ACAP)	Good senior analysts	High	0.86
Applications Experience (AEXP)	Three years	Nominal	1.00
Programmer Capability (PCAP)	Good senior programmers	High	0.86
Virtual Machine Experience (VEXP)	Six months	Low	1.10
Prog. Language Experience (LEXP)	Twelve months	Nominal	1.00
Modern Prog. Practices (MODP)	Most techniques are in use more than one year	High	0.91
Use of Software Tools (TOOL)	At basic minicomputer level	Low	1.10
Required Development Schedule (SCED)	Nine months	Nominal	1.00

Calculate the Effort and Schedule Estimates

When a non-nominal rating is assigned to any of a project's cost factors, it implies that the nominal effort estimate for the project must be modified.

The Intermediate COCOMO model has a method to calculate an effort adjustment factor based on the cost factor ratings: multiply all effort multipliers together to yield an effort adjustment factor. Then this adjustment factor is used to estimate how the effort for this project is different from the average project.

(Continued)

Sample Application of COCOMO Model (Continued)

In the communications project example, nine factors (refer to Table 5) were given non-nominal ratings. To find the effort adjustment factor (EAF) for the project, multiply together all effort multipliers (shown in the table on p. 207):

EAF = (1.0)(.94)(1.3)(1.11)(1.06)(1.0)(1.0)(.86)(.86)(1.0)(1.1)(1.0)(.91)(1.1)(1.0) = 1.17

The value, 1.17, means that the effort for this communications project will require 17% more effort than the average project.

The new effort estimate is 193 MM. It is found by multiplying the nominal effort of the project (165 MM) by the effort adjustment factor (1.17):

$$MM_{adj} = MM_{nom} \times EAF = (165) \times (1.17) = 193 \text{ MM}$$

The next step for the cost estimator is to use this new effort estimate of 193 MM to determine an estimate of the schedule for the project. The COCOMO model provides specific equations, again based on development mode, for this translation. The embedded mode equation for estimating the schedule is:

$$TDEV_{emb} = 2.5(MM)^{0.32}$$

where: $TDEV_{emb}$ = the number of months estimated for the software development.

For this example:

$$TDEV_{emb} = 2.5(193)^{0.32} = 13 \text{ months}$$

Thus, the communications project will require 13 months to develop.

Calculate the Duration

Once the effort and schedule estimates for a project have been calculated, an estimate of the number of people required on the project is calculated by simply dividing the effort estimate (193 MM) by the schedule estimate (13 months). The effort of 193 team member-months over a 13 month period equals approximately 15 people:

Resource estimate: (193 MM + 13 months) = 14.8 non-management
team members (about 15 people)

Note: The average project would have required 12.7 people.

Calculate the Phase Distribution

The next step in the COCOMO model is to determine the distribution of people across the phases of the project's life cycle.

Refer to Tables 5 and 6 for the percentage bases for the calculations to follow.

Table 5 is used to calculate the phase distribution of the effort estimate. Table 6 is used to calculate the phase distribution of the schedule estimate. The tables are further broken down by the approximate size of a project and then by its development mode.

The size of the communications software project was estimated to be about 30 KDSI. Therefore, when calculating phase distributions using Table 5, the cost estimator for this project chooses to use the percentage values for medium size projects (32 KDSI).

The approximate distributions of effort across phases is calculated by multiplying the total effort estimate of 193 MM by the appropriate percentage from Table 5:

Product Design Phase Effort
Estimate: (193 MM) × (.18) = 35 MM

Programming Phase Effort
Estimate: (193 MM) × (.54) = 104 MM

Integration and Test Phase Effort
Estimate: (193 MM) × (.28) = 54 MM

Similarly, using Table 6, the schedule estimates for each phase are calculated by multiplying the total schedule estimate (13 months) by each of the percent values provided in the table. These approximations are:

Product Design Phase Schedule
Estimate: (13 months) × (.34) = 4.5 months

Programming Phase Schedule
Estimate: (13 months) × (.40) = 5 months

Integration and Test Phase Schedule
Estimate: (13 months) × (.26) = 3.5 months

The graph in Figure 22 shows the relationship of the effort estimate to the schedule estimate.

Estimate the Cost

The last step illustrated here is to calculate the cost estimates for the communications software project. Although presented last, it is not necessarily the last step in software estimation.

For example, once the cost estimator had determined the nominal effort estimate (165 MM) for this project, a high-level cost estimate could be calculated by multiplying that number by the average cost per person per month.

For our example, assume that management uses an average cost of $7,000 per person per month (including overhead costs) when estimating project costs. The high-level cost estimate for this project would be as follows:

$$(165 \text{ MM}) \times (\$7,000) = \$1,115,500$$

As the cost estimator proceeds through the COCOMO model, estimates of increasingly greater accuracy and detail may be calculated. For instance, when the cost estimator changed the cost factor ratings, the effort adjustment factor of 1.17 caused the effort estimate to change from 165 MM to 193 MM. This in turn causes a 17% increase in estimated costs:

$$(193 \text{ MM}) \times (\$7,000) = \$1,351,000$$

Using the schedule estimates and the phase distribution values calculated in the COCOMO model, management can further refine these cost estimates as needed.

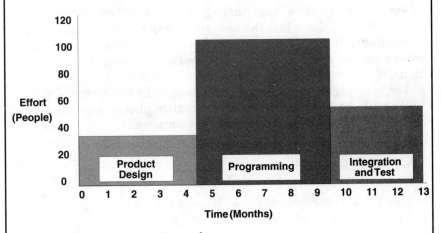

Figure 22 Effort estimate on a time scale.

Effort and cost estimation cautions

The COCOMO model considers many factors that affect the effort, schedule, resource, and cost estimates of a project. Its considerations are by no means exhaustive, however, and there are some factors not specifically addressed in COCOMO. They include:

- language level
- requirements volatility
- amount of documentation
- customer interface quality
- management quality
- security/privacy restrictions
- personnel continuity
- hardware configuration

Each of the many available cost estimation models use some subset of the cost factors discussed throughout this part. Before choosing a model, cost estimators should look at the factors considered significant in each model and determine the ones that provide the best fit for their projects. Although sometimes none will fit exactly, a reasonable effort and cost estimate of effort and cost may be determined by a comparison of the results from different models.

Software Verification and Validation Plan

The Software Verification and Validation Plan (SVVP) is the strategic planning document that describes the standard for quality assurance over the life cycle of the product.

Verification ensures "that there has been a faithful translation of [each life cycle] phase into the next one." "Validation is…the process of determining the level of conformance between the system requirements and an operational software system under operational conditions."[44]

The example beginning on the next page is the IEEE standard SVVP and should be used as a model.[45] The entire plan is presented, but it may need to be customized to apply to your project.

---

[44]Quirk, ed. *Verification and Validation of Real-Time Software,* 32–34.

[45]"IEEE Standard for Software Verification and Validation Plans," 18.

Sample Software Verification and Validation Plan

IEEE Standard SVVP

1. Purpose—brief definition of project; scope and goals of SVVP
2. Referenced Documents—list of binding compliance documents, historical references, supporting documents
3. Definitions—interpretation of terms, acronyms, notations
4. Verification and Validation (V&V) Overview
   A. Organization—definition of the V&V effort for developers, management, quality assurance, operations, users; definition of lines of communication, authority for problem resolution, authority for product approval
   B. Master Schedule—phases of project life cycle (with dated milestones)
   C. Resources Summary—staffing, facilities, tools, finances, special procedures (e.g., security, access rights, documentation control)
   D. Responsibilities—"who does what," tied to the "when" of the master schedule
   E. Tools, Techniques, Methodologies—summary of use and purpose of ancillary processes and products, together with a plan for acquisition, training, and support (or reference to a V&V Tool Plan)
5. Life Cycle V&V—the linkage between specific tasks and V&V goals. Each phase (plus the management "phase") should be examined as follows:

   - identify methods and procedures for each task and define the evaluation criteria
   - identify inputs (often written) for each task, together with source and format
   - identify outputs (often written) for each task, together with source and format
   - provide task schedule, with dated milestones for initiation and completion, for (input) receipt, and for (output) delivery
   - describe source, use, and availability of resources (e.g., staff, equipment, facilities, schedule, travel, training, tools)
   - identify the risks and assumptions for each task and risk contingencies
   - assign specific task responsibilities to individuals or small groups

   Note: The identified phases may be overlapping and iterative.
   The tasks are listed below.
   A. Management of V&V—tasks include SVVP generation, baseline change assessment, management review of V&V, review support.
   B. Concept Phase V&V—tasks include creation and evaluation of concept documentation.
   C. Requirements Phase V&V—tasks include software requirements traceability analysis, software requirements evaluation, software requirements interface analysis, test plan generation (system, acceptance).
   D. Design Phase V&V—tasks include software design traceability analysis, software design evaluation, software design interface analysis, test plan generation (component, integration), test design generation (component, integration, system, acceptance).
   E. Implementation Phase V&V—tasks include source code traceability analysis, source code evaluation, source code interface analysis, source code documentation evaluation, test case generation (component, integration, system, acceptance), test procedure generation (component, integration, system), component test execution.

(Continued)

Sample Software Verification and Validation Plan (Continued)

F. Test Phase V&V—tasks include acceptance test procedure generation, test execution (integration, system, acceptance).

G. Installation and Checkout Phase V&V—tasks include installation and configuration audit, final V&V report generation.

H. Operation and Maintenance Phase V&V—tasks include SVVP revision, anomaly evaluation, proposed change assessment, phase task iteration.

6. Software V&V Reporting—tasks include: identification of the content, format, and timing of all V&V reports; task reports, phase summary reports, anomaly reports, final report, special studies report.

7. V&V Administrative Procedures

A. Anomaly Reporting and Resolution—method for reporting and resolving anomalies: definitions of anomaly, criticality criteria, distribution list, timing of resolutions

B. Task Iteration Policy—the extent to which a task will be performed again when its input is changed; assessment of change magnitude, criticality, effect on cost, schedule, and quality.

C. Deviation Policy—proper deviation as defined by rationale; effect on quality and authority

D. Control Procedures—plan for configuration, protection, storage of product and data

E. Standards, Practices, Conventions—internal organizational standards that govern task performance

Code Inspection

Conducting formal code inspections is a part of the overall effort to develop high quality software systems. With proper planning in place and a verification and validation scheme in use, technical risks are reduced and overall quality is improved.

Code inspections are rigorous and formal peer reviews of the software. They are conducted to make sure the code agrees with the requirements and the design and to reduce the number of faults transmitted from one development stage to the next (and thereby reduce the cost of removing faults in later phases or after the product has been released). Another goal is to make sure the software can be enhanced and modified later, if needed. Inspections should *not* be an evaluation of the coder's performance.

During a code inspection, software errors are classified by severity (major or minor) and by class (missing, wrong, or extra). Refer to *Design to Reduce Technical Risk* for more details about the mechanics of conducting inspections.

Inspection checklist

The following Sample Code Inspection Checklist identifies some concerns during a code inspection. Though long, the list is not meant to be all-inclusive. This is an example; your own list will need to be customized.[46] [47] [48]

---

[46]Page-Jones, *The Practical Guide to Structured Systems Design*, 299–301.

[47]Myers, 30–32.

[48]Fagan, Michael. 1976. "Design and Code Inspections to Reduce Errors in Program Development." *IBM Systems Journal* vol. 15, No 3, (July): 182–211.

Sample Code Inspection Checklist

Data Reference and Usage
1. Make sure there are no off-by-one faults in array subscript or indexing.
2. Check input parameters to ensure they are within bounds.
3. Check value of variables to ensure they are within bounds.
4. Define pointers appropriately for the objects they point to.
5. Do type-casting correctly.
6. Use macros properly with the right parameters.
7. Don't use absolute (literal) constants in place of symbolics.
8. Don't use uninitialized variables or unset variables.
9. Don't use uninitialized pointers or unset pointers.
10. Don't use non-integer array subscripts.
11. Eliminate dangling references.
12. Match record and structure attributes.
13. Make sure there are no computation of bit-string addresses or passing of bit-string arguments.
14. Make sure based storage attributes are correct.
15. Make sure string size limits have not been exceeded.

Data Declaration/Definition and Initialization

1. Declare all variables.
2. Match structure definitions across procedures.
3. Make sure variables initialized by declaration are fault-free on restarts.
4. Make global variable definitions consistent across modules.
5. Declare variables in data structures (to conserve memory).
6. Declare indexing variables as short integers (to conserve memory).
7. Make sure sign extension is correct.
8. Make sure lengths, types, and storage classes are declared correctly.
9. Define all constants.
10. Make sure variables have dissimilar names.
11. Make sure arrays and strings are properly initialized. Indexing variables should be properly initialized (0 or 1).
12. Make sure initialization is consistent with storage class.

(Continued)

Sample Code Inspection Checklist (Continued)

General Computation

1. No arithmetic faults.
2. No indeterminate expressions.
3. No computations on non-arithmetic variables.
4. No mixed-mode computations.
5. No mixed computations on variables of different sizes.
6. Target size the same as the size of assigned value.
7. No intermediate result overflow or underflow.
8. No division by zero.
9. Operator precedence understood correctly and properly parenthesized.
10. Correct integer divisions.

Comparison and Booleans

1. No mixed comparisons of variables of different types.
2. Correct and properly parenthesized comparison relationships.
3. Correct and properly parenthesized Boolean expressions.
4. Compiler evaluation for Boolean expressions understood.
5. Correct condition tested ("if x = on" vs. "if x = off").
6. Correct variables used for test ("if x = on" vs. "if y = on").

Iteration

1. Each loop should terminate.
2. Program should terminate.
3. No loop bypasses because of entry conditions.
4. Possible loop fall-throughs should be correct.
5. No off-by-one iteration errors.

Control Flow

1. Every case statement should have a default case.
2. Each case in a case statement should have a break, a return, or a comment that the code is falling through.
3. There should be no unnecessary GOTO statements.
4. IF/THEN/ELSE statements should handle all cases and be exhaustive.
5. The branch most frequently exercised should be the THEN clause.
6. Null THEN or ELSE statements should be included as appropriate.
7. DO/END statements should match. IF/THEN/ELSE statements should match.

Intra- and Inter-Process Interfaces

1. All modifiable parameters should be "call by reference."
2. Global variables should contain the correct data.
3. Function declaration and return value should match.
4. Operating system calls, sends, and receives should be correct.
5. All libraries should be shared.
6. Registers should be saved on entry and restored on exit.
7. The number, attributes, and order of arguments transmitted to called modules should match number, attributes, and order of parameters.
8. The number, attributes, and order of arguments to built-in functions should be correct.
9. There should be no alteration of input-only arguments.
10. No constants passed as arguments.
11. Feature interaction(s) should not be missing.
12. Future feature interactions should not be precluded.

Input/Output

1. File attributes should be correct.
2. OPEN statements should be correct.
3. Format specification should match I/O statement.
4. Buffer size should match record size.
5. Files should be opened before use and closed after use.
6. End-of-file conditions should be handled.
7. I/O errors should be handled.
8. Output information should contain no textual errors.

Project Specification/Design

1. The code should achieve what is specified in the specification document and what is specified in the design document.
2. There should be no missing or incorrect specification(s) in the documentation against which the code is being verified.
3. There should be no architecture violations.

Achievement of Design Goals

1. Code should meet all design goals (e.g., should be functional, accurate, reliable, portable, maintainable, efficient, cost-effective, reusable).

Commentary

1. Comments should be meaningful to someone other than the author.
2. Comments should comply with the standards for commenting code.

Coding Standards

1. Code should comply with coding standards.

System Resource

1. Memory usage should not be excessive.
2. Resources should be allocated and freed correctly.

Post-Compilation Checks

1. There should be no unreferenced variables in the cross-reference listing.
2. Attribute list should be as expected.
3. There should be no post-compilation warning or informational messages.
4. There should be no missing functions.
5. There should be no misplaced punctuation (e.g., semicolons, parentheses, brackets, braces).

Inspecting rewritten code

If the code to be inspected has been rewritten to fix a problem, several other questions must be answered. See example below.

Checklist for Rewritten Code

1. If a global variable has been changed or deleted, all functions using that variable should be modified.
2. Additions, changes, or deletions of parameters should be reflected in calling modules.
3. If modifications to an inter-process message structure increase the size of the structure, the size should be within the message size limit.
4. The solution should not break another feature.
5. The solution should not preclude adding feature interactions if needed.
6. The solution should not adversely affect system performance.

Software System Test Plans

An important part of the SVVP is the collection of system test plans that address individual software features. These test plans are the tactical implementation of the SVVP strategy. Two examples are given on the next few pages.

- Sample 1 shows the concerns that should be addressed in a system test plan and a convenient format for their discussion.
- Sample 2 demonstrates some ways in which a system test plan may fall short.

An analysis of the strong and weak points of each test plan follows the samples.

Sample 1: A Good System Test Plan

I. Name and Description of Feature to be Tested

BigSys 'date' command

Given a date as input from the user (valid format: mm/dd/yy), display the day of the week on the user's terminal.

II. Responsible Tester

Connie Conrad of the BigSys System Test Group (QQQ Department), Maintown.

III. Test Objective(s)

Primary Objectives

Basic Functionality—meets facility specifications according to BigSys Detailed Design Document, p. 16.

Performance—meets performance requirements according to BigSys Requirements Document, pp. 20–21.

Fault Tolerance—meets error recovery specifications according to BigSys Requirements Document, p. 11, and BigSys Preliminary Design Document, p. 19.

Secondary Objectives—to be done in parallel with tests to meet primary objectives.

Documentation—actual system responses should match user document, BigSys User Guide.

IV. Referenced Materials

BigSys Requirements Document
BigSys Preliminary Design Document
BigSys Detailed Design Document
BigSys User Guide

V. Test Environment

Hardware: DEC VAX 8530, AT&T 615 CRT
Software: BigSys Version III, Release 2.0
Memory: 16Mb
Storage media: ten RPO-5 drives

VI. Method of Test Invocation and Evaluation, Result Documentation

Testing is partially automated: command invocation is automated via the T_SCRIPT tool (see Test Tools), input/output capture is automated via T_SCRIPT, evaluation is manual, and documentation is semi-automated via the DOC_IT tool (see Test Tools).

VII. Test Tools

The T_SCRIPT program will be used to invoke the command under test and to capture the input and output. On completion (pass or fail), online test results will be manually moved to files that are named according to the project guidelines and kept there until no longer needed.

The DOC_IT program will be used to generate end-of-the-day reports about the progress of testing, including the success rate, the current status of bug fixes, and the number and results of the day's tested cases.

VIII. Test Cases

Test cases, script files, and expected output files are:

Test Case	T_SCRIPT Script	Test Output
1	scr.date.1	out.date.1
2	scr.date.2	out.date.2
3	scr.date.3	out.date.3
4	scr.date.4	out.date.4
5	scr.date.5	out.date.5
6	scr.date.6	out.date.6
7	scr.date.7	out.date.7
8	scr.date.8	out.date.8

All scripts and test outputs are located on the alfa3 machine. The precondition for all test cases is that BigSys is operating in a non-degraded mode.

Test Case	Test Objective	Input	Expected Output	Comments
1	function	date 02/29/88	Monday	leap year
2	function	date 02/01/89	Wednesday	
3	fault	date 2/1/89	invalid input format	
4	fault	date 02/29/89	invalid date	not a leap year
5	fault	date 13/13/89	invalid date	
6	fault	date 02/89	invalid input format	
7	perform	date 02/01/89	Wednesday	max. time: 4 sec.
8	perform	date 02/89	invalid input format	max. time: 4 sec.

(Continued)

Sample 1: A Good System Test Plan (Continued)

IX. Test Case Failure Procedure

If a test case fails, the procedure is as stated in the SVVP; it is included here for completeness.

Test case failure will be summarized to first-line management on a daily basis. Each failed test case will be documented via the opening of an online Modification Request (MR) within one day of failure. The MR system will automatically print a copy of the MR for the developer, the developer's supervisor, and the tester. When the problem is resolved, the test case will be retested; if the tester deems the problem fixed, then the MR will be closed.

Sample 2: A Poor Test Plan

I. Name and Description of Feature to be Tested

BigSys family of report-generation commands that create reports automatically.

II. Responsible Tester

Harry Harrier.

III. Test Objective

Stress at designed peak; system should be easy to use.

IV. Referenced Materials

All BigSys Design documents.

V. Test Environment

BigSys on a DEC VAX.

VI. Method of Test Invocation and Evaluation, Result Documentation

Testers will log into system and pretend to be users, invoking the report generating programs.

VII. Test Tools

None used.

VIII. Test Cases

1. List the available reports.
2. Request reports for which the user is not authorized.
3. Generate sales report—New York, USA, International.
4. Generate sales report and spool for later printing.
5. Generate sales report and spool for later printing, then cancel.

IX. Test Case Failure Procedure

For every detected error, tester will write a memo to the developer.

Analysis of sample test plans

Sample 1 and Sample 2 are distinguishable primarily by the degree of preciseness: the good test plan is very explicit, stating assumptions and goals with clarity; the poor test plan lacks detail and is vague. That imprecision is apparent in every section of Sample 2 as discussed in the comparison below:

I. **Name and Description of Feature to be Tested.** The specific ("date") is preferable to the vague "family of commands" because it is exact. All readers need a definitive list of commands to be tested, be they document reviewers, the system test manager, other members of the test group, or the person performing the test.

A brief description should provide a simple overview, mentioning the general nature of input, output, and the method of invocation (manual or automated).

II. **Responsible Tester.** The tester should be named; the organization and location should be identified.

III. **Test Objective.** Every test must have one or more goals. Sample 1 has three primary goals; its secondary goal is ancillary and is accomplished in parallel with the primary ones. Sample 2 lacks clear goals.

A test objective should identify a test category and include a statement about the quantifiable goal (or a reference to the specifying document).

The following are some examples of test categories.

Examples of Test Categories:

- basic functionality (i.e., facility)
- data overload tolerance/performance (i.e., volume)
- user overload tolerance/performance (i.e., stress)
- judgment of human interface (i.e., usability)
- security
- performance
- data and program storage
- configuration
- compatibility with other systems
- conversion from a previous release
- coupling (i.e., installability)
- reliability
- fault tolerance (i.e., error recovery)
- maintainability (i.e., serviceability)
- documentation
- ancillary (support) procedures

IV. **Referenced Materials.** All sources should be specifically cited.

V. **Test Environment.** All hardware and software should be specifically listed.

VI. Method of Test Invocation and Evaluation, Result Documentation. A choice of automated, semi-automated (that is, with tester intervention), or manual should be stated for each: invocation, evaluation, and documentation.

VII. Test Tools. Any automation (identified in Method of Test Invocation and Evaluation, Result Documentation) should be specifically listed.

This section should contain:

- list of auxiliary software and hardware required for testing
- description of test equipment and "capture" method for input and output
- notes on procedures

VIII. Test Cases. Generality in this section guarantees an unsuccessful test program. Sample 2 suffers from extreme imprecision, raising many questions:

- Test Case 1: Does it mean "execute the 'list' command to view the menu of available reports" or "review the documentation to familiarize yourself with the options" or something else? What are the expected responses?
- Test Case 2: How is authorization set up? Verified?
- Test Case 3: Does it mean "generate three sales reports, one of each?" What are the expected responses? How much time will be spent on the test? Will the testers be concurrently logged on? Might automated or manual scripts be used? What features of the report generators will be exercised? What are the expected results?
- Test Case 4: To which sales report does this refer? How does the user "spool"?
- Test Case 5: How does the user "cancel"?

IX. Test Case Failure Procedure. This section should contain:

- reference to management information and escalation
- time frame for evaluation of failure and reporting to management
- tracking process for bug fixes

Summary

Software is becoming an ever-increasing part of our military systems. This growth in software use has resulted in both increased system costs and increased system complexity. The two keys to successful software development are: careful planning for each step in the process; and verifying and validating the results of each step. (See Figure 23.) The actual writing of code is only one small aspect of software development. Thus, software design becomes the process of planning for quality before, during, and after the writing of code. Software test becomes the process of ensuring that a quality product is achieved.

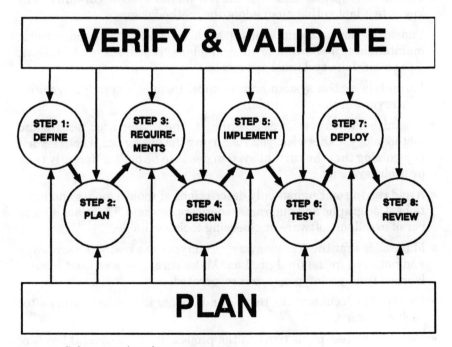

Figure 23 Software engineering process.

Over the past decades, software engineers have shifted away from fixing software failures after the system has been deployed to developing proven methodologies and techniques that ensure software quality from the start. These efforts have also yielded increased productivity and better adherence to schedules.

The Procedures chapter describes an eight-step process for developing a software system. Two concepts—Verification and Validation, and Planning—are of critical importance to system development. They influence every step, and together they determine the success or failure of the project.

Things to remember

In following best practices, experienced software engineers highly recommend the following:

- Plan carefully and completely with attention to details. There is always a temptation to start development of the software before the project is really understood.

- Don't be short-sighted when planning the feasibility report. A feasibility report for a large project requires time and effort.

- Choose appropriate and well-proven methodologies carefully. The key is to adapt rather than adopt the methodology.

- Consider "downstream" phases such as installation, operations, maintenance, and training in your plans, schedules, and budgets. Take a total life cycle cost approach.

- Formulate a good system architecture. Include a detailed architecture review in the project plan.

- Organize human resources according to the system architecture and methodology. Otherwise, you risk using the wrong people or risk not recognizing that the current system needs to be built differently than previous systems.

- Avoid relying on English-only descriptions of requirements and functions. Use graphs and diagrams where appropriate. There are a number of excellent software engineering tools available.

- Make sure that the "throw-away" prototypes are really thrown away and not used in the final product. Make sure, however, that lessons learned from prototyping are incorporated.

- Review and document the results and update the project status after each milestone.

- Develop the test plans early in the project. Plan for several levels of testing and avoid a "big bang" approach.

- Use good documentation.
- Use good configuration control.

Summary of procedures

Good quality software is the result of careful attention to the quality of the planning and the standards for that software, as well as attention to the quality of the code itself. Part 2 has presented the step-by-step procedures for implementing the principles and templates for good quality software. Table 7 is a summary of those steps.

TABLE 7   Summary of the Software Procedures

Step 1—Define the Concept

Procedure	Supporting activities
Identify a Need for Product	<ul><li>Review need for product</li><li>Refer to *Design to Reduce Technical Risk* for methods</li></ul>
Assess User Needs	<ul><li>Define user base via user surveys and interviews</li><li>Observe users and their tasks</li><li>Analyze user needs data</li></ul>
Analyze Feasibility	<ul><li>Assess risks</li><li>Assess complexity</li><li>Estimate required resources</li><li>Determine constraints</li><li>Define and use feasibility criteria to analyze "go" or "no-go"</li><li>Produce Feasibility Report</li></ul>

Step 2—Plan the Project

Procedure	Supporting activities
Form the Project Team	<ul><li>Assess personnel needs for project design, development, review, inspection, test, deployment, maintenance</li><li>Assess skill levels and training needs of potential team members</li><li>Choose and train competent teams</li></ul>
Define the Cost Estimation Plan	<ul><li>Identify those cost-affecting factors that are appropriate to the project</li><li>Select one or more costing techniques that emphasize those factors</li><li>Document the selection and the criteria</li></ul>

TABLE 7   Summary of the Software Procedures (Continued)

Step 2—Plan the Project (*continued*)

Procedure	Supporting activities
Define the Life Cycle Model	▪ Compare available life cycle models to identify structures and concerns that are appropriate to the project ▪ Select a model ▪ Define entry and exit criteria for the stages of the model ▪ Document the selection and the criteria
Define the Documentation Requirements	▪ Analyze project and life cycle model for information needs ▪ Identify type and content of documents ▪ Define criteria for the acceptability of the documents ▪ Document the selection and the criteria (part of draft SVVP)
Define Coding Standards	▪ Use corporate coding guidelines ▪ Define criteria for the acceptability of the code ▪ Document the standards (part of draft SVVP)
Define Testing Standards	▪ Define entry and exit criteria for the acceptability of the modules ▪ Document the standards (part of draft SVVP)
Define the Method for Reviews, Inspections, Walkthroughs	▪ Analyze project for quality requirements ▪ Select a method ▪ Define entry and exit criteria for reviews ▪ Document the selection
Define the Change Control Scheme	▪ Analyze alternatives and select one to use ▪ Document the selection (part of draft SVVP)
Define the Project Metrics	▪ Assess project and corporate measurement needs ▪ Use corporate measurement guidelines ▪ Select appropriate metrics ▪ Document the selection
Conduct SVVP Review	▪ Review draft SVVP Plan, which contains documentation requirements, coding and testing standards, and change control scheme ▪ Produce SVVP Plan
Choose Software Tools	▪ Analyze alternatives available, for example, CASE development products

TABLE 7 **Summary of the Software Procedures (Continued)**

Step 3—Develop the Software Requirements

Procedure	Supporting activities
Develop System Requirements	■ Describe the current environment
	■ Define the scope of the new system
	■ Develop I/O requirements
	■ Define the system's functions
	■ Catalog user requirements and constraints
	■ List requirements for performance, operations, testing, and maintenance
	■ Specify external controls
	■ Produce draft Requirements Document
Conduct Requirements Review	■ Review draft Requirements Document
	■ Produce final Requirements Document
	■ Follow change control guidelines for revisions

Step 4—Design the Software System

Procedure	Supporting activities
Perform Preliminary Design	■ Define the system architectures—overall, hardware, software
	■ Define the user interface
	■ Choose the physical implementation
	■ Perform ongoing functional decomposition
	■ Perform data modeling
	■ Identify test tactics and strategies
	■ Produce draft Preliminary Design Document
Conduct Preliminary Design Review	■ Refer to *Design to Reduce Technical Risk* for methods
	■ Review draft Preliminary Design Document for fidelity to requirements, rationale, assumptions, and goal attainment
	■ Produce final Preliminary Design Document
	■ Follow change control guidelines for revisions
Perform Detailed Design	■ Choose design tool
	■ Develop implementation details: specifics of system, process, and data
	■ Produce draft Detailed Design Document
Conduct Critical Design Review	■ Refer to *Design to Reduce Technical Risk* for methods
	■ Review draft Detailed Design Document for fidelity to requirements, rationale, assumptions, and goal attainment
	■ Produce final Preliminary Design Document
	■ Follow change control guidelines for revisions

TABLE 7   Summary of the Software Procedures (Continued)

Procedure	Supporting activities
Step 4—Design the Software System (*continued*)	
Review and Revise Cost and Scheduling Estimates and Metrics	■ Collect and analyze data ■ Publish any revisions
Step 5—Implement the Software System	
Produce Code	■ Follow design ■ Attain requirements goals ■ Adhere to coding standards ■ Follow change control guidelines for revisions
Conduct Code Inspections	■ Inspect, as per review guidelines ■ Document the results
Develop Unit Test Plans	■ Document overall test strategy, test cases, entry and exit criteria, scheduling
Review and Revise Cost and Scheduling Estimates and Metrics	■ Collect and analyze data ■ Publish any revisions
Step 6—Test the Software	
Perform Unit Tests	■ Test, as per Unit Test Plans (as per SVVP) ■ Publish test results
Perform Integration Test	■ Combine components incrementally until the system is built ■ Test the system and its interfaces, as per Integration Test Plan ■ Publish test results
Perform System Test	■ Test, as per SVVP, for adherence to requirements, functionality, and other factors ■ Conduct regression testing ■ Publish test results
Review and Revise Cost and Scheduling Estimates and Metrics	■ Collect and analyze data ■ Publish any revisions
Step 7—Deploy and Maintain the Software System	
Train the Users	■ Provide user documentation ■ Provide instruction in system use ■ Obtain feedback on training from users
Deploy the System	■ Replace older system ■ Use change control and configuration management to track revisions, version control by site, error reports, fixes, releases, documentation updates

TABLE 7   Summary of the Software Procedures (Continued)

Procedure	Supporting activities
Step 7—Deploy and Maintain the Software System (*continued*)	
Perform Acceptance Test	▪ Perform user test, as per SVVP ▪ Negotiate any needed redevelopment
Generate Periodic System Performance Reports	▪ Monitor operational trends: user activity, transaction time, throughput rate, cycle time, queuing time, system access time, data access time, error rates ▪ Publish ongoing reports
Perform Ongoing Maintenance	▪ Correct problems ▪ Develop enhancements ▪ Adapt software to evolving environment
Revise Cost and Scheduling Estimates and Metrics	▪ Collect and analyze data ▪ Publish any revisions
Step 8—Review for Improvement	
Perform Product Postmortem	▪ Compare the deployed product to design objectives ▪ Analyze the deployed system for correctness, reliability, usability, flexibility, maintainability, efficiency, integrity, testability, portability, reusability ▪ Publish the results of the analysis
Perform Process Postmortem	▪ Compare the development process to planning objectives ▪ Analyze the development process for management techniques, responsibilities, methodology, adherence to standards, experience, training, tool and technology use, communication, delivery dates, risk assessment, cost estimates ▪ Publish the results of the analysis

Bergland, G. D., "A Guided Tour of Program Methodologies," *IEEE Computer,* October 1981. Discusses four software design methods: structured analysis, functional decomposition, data flow design, and data structure design.

Bersoff, Edward H.; Henderson, Vilas D.; and Siegel, Stanley G., *Configuration Management: An Investment in Product Integrity.* Englewood Cliffs, N.J.: Prentice-Hall, 1980. Discusses the principles of configuration control, auditing, and status accounting in software development projects.

Best Practices: How to Avoid Surprises in the World's Most Complicated Technical Process. Department of the Navy (NAVSO P-6071), March 1986. Discusses how to avoid traps and risks by implementing best practices for 47 areas or templates that include topics in design, test, production, facilities, and management. These templates give program managers and contractors an overview of the key issues and best practices to improve the acquisition life cycle.

Boar, Bernard H., *Application Prototyping: A Requirements Definition Strategy for the 80s.* New York: John Wiley & Sons, 1984. Discusses software prototyping as a method for defining the user requirements for a system.

Boehm, Barry W., "A Spiral Model of Software Development and Enhancement," *Computer,* May 1988. Discusses the risk driven spiral model for software development, its focus on early prototyping and simulation, current usage of the model, and advantages of this process model over other software models available.

Boehm, Barry W., "Software Engineering," *IEEE Transactions on Computers, December 1976.* Provides a survey of software engineering technology in several of the life cycle phases and discusses software trends.

Boehm, Barry W., *Software Engineering Economics.* Englewood Cliffs, N.J.: Prentice-Hall, 1981. Gives an in-depth explanation of the COnstructive COst MOdel (COCOMO) for estimating resources, staffing levels and costs of a software development project. Discusses the impact of numerous cost drivers associated with a project such as: product attributes, computer attributes, and personnel attributes.

Boehm, Barry W. and Papaccio, Philip N., "Understanding and Controlling Software Costs," *IEEE Transactions on Software Engineering,* October 1988. Discusses key issues in estimating software development costs.

Booch, Grady. "Object-Oriented Development," *IEEE Transactions on Software Engineering,* February 1988. Discusses key issues in object-oriented development.

Brooks, Frederick P., "No Silver Bullet," *IEEE Computer,* April 1987. Discusses the nature of software development projects and why there are no easy ways (silver bullets) for making large improvements in productivity, reliability and simplicity.

Brooks, Frederick P., *The Mythical Man-Month: Essays on Software Engineering.* Reading, Massachusetts: Addison-Wesley Publishing Company, 1975. Discusses the difficulties of managing large software projects and other software management issues.

Buckley, Fletcher J., *Implementing Software Engineering Practices*. New York: John Wiley & Sons, 1989. Provides guidance and examples for establishing software engineering standards and practices within an organization. Discusses current IEEE and DoD standards.

Cortese, Amy, "Estimating Tools reap 85% Accuracy, Some Say," *Computerworld*, November 14, 1988. Brief discussion of current state of software costs estimation tools.

DeMarco, Tom, *Structured Analysis and System Specification*. New York: Yourdon, 1978. Provides details of structured software design techniques.

DeMillo, Richard A.; McCracken, W. Michael; Martin, R. J.; and Passafiume, John F., *Software Testing and Evaluation*. Menlo Park, California: The Benjamin/Cummings Publishing Company, 1987. Provides a discussion of software testing techniques and an overview of current defense practices gathered from interviews and surveys with military and industrial personnel. Also includes data sheets on numerous testing tools.

Deutsch, Michael S., *Software Verification and Validation: Realistic Project Approaches*. Englewood Cliffs, N.J.: Prentice-Hall, 1982. Discusses software testing methodologies and the use of verification and validation techniques throughout the entire software life cycle.

Fairley, Richard E., *Software Engineering Concepts*. New York: McGraw-Hill Book Company, 1985. Provides a comprehensive description of the entire software development life cycle from concept definition through maintenance. Also includes many good examples of software engineering concepts. Very good section about planning the software development effort.

"IEEE Standard for Software Unit Testing," *ANSI/IEEE Std. 1008-1987*, December 29, 1986. Discusses planning for, implementing and measuring software unit testing.

IEEE Standard for Software Verification and Validation Plans, Std. 1012-1986, November 14, 1986. Provides a complete guide for the development of a standard verification and validation plan throughout the life cycle of a software development project.

Kemerer, Chris F., "An Empirical Validation of Software Cost Estimation Models," *Communications of the ACM*, May 1987. Provides an evaluation of four popular software cost estimation models: SLIM, COCOMO, Function Points and ESTIMACS.

Kirk, Frank G., *Total System Development for Information Systems*. New York: John Wiley & Sons, 1973. Discusses a disciplined method for developing a software system. Includes an activities network which is used as the framework for describing the total system development effort.

"Managing Software Development: Solving the Productivity Puzzle," Course Moderator's Guide, John Wiley & Sons, Inc., 1985. Provides good overview of key points in the software development process with emphasis on the management of a software project.

Meyer, Bertrand, *Object-Oriented Software Construction*, Englewood Cliffs, NJ: Prentice Hall, 1988. Describes how object-oriented software is developed.

Musa, John D.; Iannino, Anthony; and Okumoto, Kazuhira, *Software Reliability: Measurement, Prediction, Application*. New York: McGraw-Hill, 1987. Describes the basics of software reliability measurement, provides the procedures and formulas for applying the measurements, and also details the theoretical background of software reliability.

Myers, Glenford J., *The Art of Software Testing*. New York: John Wiley & Sons, 1979. Describes the various types of software testing and the tools and techniques commonly used. Also provides discussions of test case design, software debugging and program inspections, walkthroughs, and reviews.

Myers, Glenford J., *Software Reliability: Principles & Practices*. New York: John Wiley & Sons, 1976. Describes what needs to be done during each of the various stages of software development to produce reliable software.

Perry, William E., *A Structured Approach to Systems Testing, Second Edition*. Wellesley, Massachusetts: QED Information Sciences, 1988. Comprehensive discussion of software testing throughout the entire life cycle. Includes test, documentation, review and audit checklists and examples.

Peters, Lawrence J., *Software Design: Methods & Technologies*. New York: Yourdon Press, 1981. Discusses the role of and issues of software design. Includes descriptions of tools and techniques used in software design.

Quirk, W. J., ed., *Verification and Validation of Real-time Software.* New York: Springer-Verlag, 1985. Provides an array of articles concerning software development methods and standards.

Smith, David J. and Wood, Kenneth B., *Engineering Quality Software: A Review of Current Practices, Standards and Guidelines including New Methods and Development Tools.* London: Elsevier Applied Science, 1987. Discusses software standards and guidelines in several different countries. Provides checklists for software design, design reviews, programming standards, testing, change control, documentation, and project management.

Transition from Development to Production. Department of Defense (DoD 4245.7-M), September 1985. Techniques for avoiding technical risks in 47 key areas or templates including funding, design, test, production, facilities, logistics, management, and transition plan. Identifies critical engineering processes and controls for the design, test, and production of low risk products.

Vincent, James; Waters, Albert; and Sinclair, John, *Software Quality Assurance: Volume I, Practice and Implementation.* Englewood Cliffs, N.J.: Prentice-Hall, 1988. Discusses the factors of software quality, software metrics and software audits. Provides numerous checklists, forms, and algorithms for assessing and measuring the appropriate factors.

Wallace, Dolores R. and Fujii, Roger U., "Software Verification and Validation: An Overview," *IEEE Software,* May 1989. Discusses methods and standards which support the use of verification and validation throughout the life cycle of a software project.

Wood, Bill; Pethia, Richard; Gold, Lauren Roberts; and Firth, Robert, "A Guide to the Assessment of Software Development Methods," *Technical Report* CMU/SEI-88-TR-8 ESD-TR-88-009, Carnegie-Mellon University Software Engineering Institute, April 1988. Discusses software methods and ways to determine if the methods satisfy a software development organization's needs.

Index

Testing to verify design a
manufacturing readiness